Taking cues from works as diverse as Miller's *A Canticle for Liebowitz*, Cuaron's *Children of Men*, and Atwood's *The Handmaid's Tale*, Meg Elison's *Book of the Unnamed Midwife* uses its post-apocalyptic setting to explore sexuality, gender roles, patriarchy, and the fluid nature of identity. Speaking as a former card-carrying member of the Society for Utopian Studies, I am as thrilled by this book's questions for our own society as I am the suspense that surrounds our nameless - or many named? - protagonist. An exciting debut from Elison, and worthwhile for any fan of feminist science fiction.

- Eric O. Scott, author of *The Lives of the Apostates* (Moon Books, 2013)

Meg Elison's *The Book of the Unnamed Midwife* stands head-and-shoulders above contemporary post-apocalyptic novels with a gritty intimacy that seeps into the subconscious and stays with the reader long after she's read the last page. *Midwife* is an astounding debut for an up-and-coming writer.

- Marie Lecrivain, *Bitchess.*

# *The Book of the Unnamed Midwife*

Meg Elison

SYBARITIC PRESS

Published by
Sybaritic Press
12530 Culver Blvd.
Suite 3
Los Angeles, CA 90066
www.sybpress.com



ISBN: 978-1-4951-1636-0
Cover Art - Devon Cooper
Printed in the United States of America
First Edition
June 2014

# Prologue

Mother Ina tapped her fingers on her hollow wooden belly. It tied around her shoulders and the small of her back and sloped out in front, making the curve of a nine-month pregnancy. Mother Ina was very old, too old to be really pregnant. Her hair was white and so short that her black scalp showed through, shining. She tapped again, her thin fingers drumming so that the hollow sound echoed through the room. She clicked against the wood with her fingernails rhythmically until the scribes looked up at her.

Six boys, all around the age of puberty. Their faces were hairless and their eyes were bright in the morning light. The schoolroom was older even than Ina herself. Parts of the building had collapsed. The biggest spaces had once been gyms and theatres and auditoriums, but over the years they'd sagged and then fallen, weighted with rain or snow. The long corridors of offices stood empty. Squirrels nested in the file cabinets and the branches of trees grew in through the windows.

Ina's village only used three schoolrooms. These were swept and kept up. Blackboards and wooden desks. The hardest things to mend were the glass windows. Some of the more skilled craftsmen had learned to pull good windows out of other buildings and reuse them, but they were never the right size. The classrooms still got sunlight, but much of it came through old sheets of plastic and acrylic. The light was enough.

The scribes had good pens. They had been trained since babyhood with walnut ink and berry ink until they were old enough to be trusted with the precious ink taken from squids or cuttlefish. Fishing them was deep business, expensive and time-consuming. Each boy had a stack of straight-cut hemp paper and a glass jar of the blue-black ink. Each boy had a stylus and a narrow squared nib. Each had been taught perfect even script and how to line out a page and work carefully, conserving.

Tap tap tap went Mother Ina's fingers on her wooden baby belly.

"Are you boys all ready?"

They gave her their silent attention. It was their signal.

"Good. You boys were chosen for a special project this year. You've all copied from the Book of the Unnamed Midwife before?"

Nods.

She walked to the large wooden desk behind her and pulled a light cloth away. Beneath it lay nineteen leather-bound books of varying size and thickness. Some were very worn. One showed the bloat and wrinkle of water exposure. Scrapes on the leather were visible on every side. The boys craned to look, but kept their seats.

Mother Ina picked up one volume with a gentle hand, and the boys could see another chamois cloth underneath the books. She held it up for them to see. In the bottom corner of the front cover, a year was stamped in gold.

The boys knew how old the Book of the Unnamed Midwife was, they had all studied it and the stories had been told all their lives. This book was four years older than what they knew.

"The Book of the Unnamed Midwife is actually these nineteen journals," she began. "What we have taught to you boys is called the canon. It holds the story of the Dying. The Book of the Dying is very hard to read and terrible things happen in it. Some of you might cry or feel sick. That's ok, I felt sick too when I came to read it. Almost all the Mothers did. You boys are just as strong as we are, and you might feel it, too.

"You have all learned the Hives and the Book of Honus. The Book of the Dreamless Ones is what you'll finish with when your training is complete." She gestured back to the stacks of books on the desk. "These are the rest of her story. The canon is short, but the whole story is longer, and messier. Each year, a group of scribes is chosen to recopy the entire cycle. This year that group is you."

There was excitement in the room. The boys felt pride at having been chosen, and were fairly bursting to know that there was more to this book than what they had been taught. Their faces twitched like the whiskers of rabbits. But they had been trained their whole lives to be silent and obedient to the Mothers, and so the room was a quiet hum.

Mother Ina was pleased.

"You'll begin today. These are the originals. The people trust us that much. So we must be worthy of that trust. That means washing your hands frequently. Senders will bring warmed water and clean towels. That also means we're going to have to close the shutters. Paper this old cannot be exposed to sunlight all day. We will work extra carefully, and preserve these books. Won't we?"

As one, they answered. "Yes, Mother Ina."

She nodded. "Get into pairs. Each scribe must start his own copy, but you will share and help each other care for the book."

She walked the first volume over to a pair of boys who had quickly pushed their desks together. They waited with the palms down on the wood. She put the book down and their eyes dropped to it. When she opened the cover, a loose leaf of hemp paper sat on top of the pages.

"You may begin."

# Chapter One

Book of the Unnamed Midwife
Volume One
The Book of the Dying

*15 January*

Patient that I was seeing earlier this week with the fever thing was transferred out. Team of guys with all the protocol bells and whistles. Heard there were a couple of cases on the same floor, but I didn't hang out with anyone this weekend so I didn't hear. Was supposed to meet Karen for drinks but all she does is complain. She should just dump him and get it over with. Hate the sound of his name, especially when she's drunk. Gerry=shit. I got it = we all got it.

*30 January*

More fever patients, but almost all women. For a while they were saying it was some kind of widespread food poisoning thing but >>> Dallas, so it's not just us. Jack's been in the lab with it for days and I've been sleeping in the call room and barely seen him. Exhausted. Worked doubles all this week, half the nurses are sick. Haven't attended a delivery in ten days. Fever 1, Babies 0. Losing team.

*31 January*

Called Laura in Conn. Talked shop. Miss her and told her to kiss her kids for me. Sounds like I feel. Asked her about how they're doing. Small town=better odds but the odds sound bad even there. Starting to freak out. Wtf is going on?

*2 February*

Shit I missed deliveries but not like this.

Don't even know what to say about the rate of infection. Can't even put the rate of stillbirth or basically stillbirth into words. What. The. Fuck. Whole hospital under quarantine, but what good is that? Got texts from over at the Mission clinic from Pilar and she says the homeless have got it just as bad. Out in the street. Fucking everywhere but the lab has nothing.

*4 February*

CDC is all over SF. News is terrible. What they were showing from New York can't really be happening. BART stopped running. Not like I'm going anywhere but damn. Preachers outside with megaphones. Hate to wish them death while so many are dying, but better them than every neonate.

Jack says it's auto-immune. Almost wish I hadn't asked, he looked so scared when he said it. Think that was more because he doesn't know. No antibiotic. No interferon. No anti-inflammatory, no sedative, no emetic, nothing. Nothing touches this once it starts. We're all wrapped in plastic but it doesn't seem to matter. Marianne went down with it two days ago. Shirley's looking like shit so they sent her home. Dr. Kaufmann just DFOd in the middle of a consult. Wake up and hear the shouting, the sound of flat-lining.

*6 February*

Feel like shit. Fever 1, Me 0.

#

*7 February*

Know I'm getting sick but no one gives a single solitary fuck. Everyone is sick. Jack came and sat down with me, felt my fever. Looked like he wanted to die. Said that some men are recovering, but not women and not children. Told me that the fever skyrocketed in pregnant women and we were at one hundred percent fetal mortality in delivery, nearly as high maternal death. Fell asleep with him holding me. Don't think I can work tomorrow. Don't think it will matter.

* * * * *

In the days when the world had not yet fallen, the screaming of sirens was constant. The structures that still held were the ones designed to cope with emergency and disaster, but none of them could work indefinitely. Desperation moved block by block, and people fought and fled. They died of the plague and they died of proximity to each other. When there weren't enough people in charge of keeping the lights on, the cities went dark. When the sirens quit, the rules gave out. Some people had been waiting their whole lives to live lawlessly, and they were the first to take to the streets. Some people knew that would happen; they knew better than to open their doors when they heard cries of help. Others didn't. What disease cannot do, people accomplish with astonishing ease.

* * * * *

She awoke in the hospital, on a cot in the nurse's break room. There was no chart on her bed and her nametag was missing. The woman knew who she was and where she was, but everything else was gone.

Her mouth and throat felt like she hadn't had a drink of water in days. It took her a while to get her bearings. She tried light switches and stared at machines that wouldn't turn on, stupefied by their disobedience. She stopped at the first body she saw, checking for a pulse. She stopped at the second and the third before she got the idea. She ran out of the building, blundering into an emergency exit. No alarm sounded.

The sun was bright and bouncing off the fog that had just begun to rise over the bay. She walked in stark and rising panic out the door and over the blocks between the hospital and her apartment. She saw no one. No busses ran, no cars moved on the streets. The stop lights were dark. She remembered treating plague victims, hearing impossible rumors. She remembered her friends dying before she got sick. She knew what had happened, but it still made no sense to her.

She made it to her apartment and stripped off her scrubs. They were dirty, always dirty after a shift with blood and amniotic fluid and urine and everything the body can leak. These were stiff with filth, and she couldn't remember how long she had been in them. She got out of her bra and underwear and climbed into the shower, trying to think straight. The water shot out of the showerhead ice-cold, and she frantically clawed at the knob to warm it up. The water lost pressure, then stopped running. She pushed and pulled, twisted every direction. She tried the tap in the sink. Nothing came.

Cold and naked, she walked to her kitchen. The bananas were black and the bread was green. She found a box of crackers and sat on the couch. She hit the button on the remote to try her TV, but it didn't turn on. She sat staring at it anyway, shoveling crackers until the salt was too much. In the warm fridge she found a bottle of Gatorade and drained it, standing there with bare feet.

Her feet led her from the kitchen and stood in her living room. Her apartment was mostly below ground level and weak sunlight came streaming down from the long skinny windows above. She stood dumbly, looking at the floor, the silence pressing in on her ears.

"What the fuck? What the fuck?"

The question repeated quietly for a long time. The answer did not come.

She put on a pair of panties and an old t-shirt and climbed into bed. She burrowed down into her own smell, the most familiar and comforting place in the world, and she refused to think.

She slept for nearly a day. It was an hour or two before dawn when he woke her. He was in bed with her, his weight pushing down on the edges of the mattress and shifting her side to side. She stirred for a second and thought it was Jack, come home to her. She sat up, smiling, the whole thing forgotten for that one golden second before full consciousness took hold.

He pushed her back down by her shoulders and he was breathing hard. She knew everything at once, every awful thing.

Everyone was dead. This was not Jack. She was alone.

He let go of one shoulder to reach down and unzip. He moved the hand holding her down to her neck and pushed the crotch of her panties to one side with the other. He was crushing her throat, using his weight above her to keep her from rising or getting her breath. She kicked once, twice, and her ankles caught in her sheet. She knew that was wasted effort. She was clawing at his face with her hands and he barely seemed to notice. She couldn't see him in the semidarkness. He was a shape, a weight, an intrusion she couldn't do anything about.

He pushed against her, trying to force his way in. She turned her hips, pulling them back, twisting right and left, drawing her knees together. He swore and wrestled with her, pushing her legs back with his knees and leaning down more heavily on to her neck. Her vision was darkness and explosions as she gasped. She let go of his face and felt how weak her arms were getting as they fell. She bucked with her whole body, trying to twist sideways, get her knees under her. He felt her flexing and struggling like a cat and worked with her suddenly, turning her over on her belly and pushing down on the middle of her back.

He switched his legs to outside of hers in one jump, came down hard on her, and pushed against her again. She felt his breath on the back of her neck and his half-erection frustrating him. He pushed his uselessness against her dry, closed lips. He took his hands off her back to reach down to her ass to force her cheeks apart.

As soon as his weight was off her, she clawed desperately to her nightstand. She ripped the drawer open to the stop and banged her wrist against the side of it, reaching in. Her right hand found her pocketknife. She thumbed it open and flicked it full while he tried to pull her thighs back toward him. She pushed off the nightstand and knocked it over. Half-facing him, she swiped the knife in a full arc at arm's length, still not really seeing. Shaking with panic and still starry-eyed from choking, she missed what she'd aimed for and caught his chin, slicing it open.

His hands flew to the wound, she could see a little of the whiteness of him with his face and hands together in the darkness. He made a strangled sound and swung at her suddenly with his right hand, punching her on her cheekbone. The punch only glanced, but her head still rocked back with it. He saw it and reached for her with both hands, his chin dribbling blood in a thin line. With both his hands down, she struck out again with the knife and this time she did not miss. The hook of the blade caught in his neck and she pulled it savagely across him with a huge angle at her shoulder. The knife cut through the skin, catching and ripping as she yanked it. His hands flew to his neck and she saw his blood, black in the low light, pumping out over his fingers.

He gurgled. She watched.

When he was no longer attacking her, her training took over. She pushed him back and applied pressure to his hands with her own. She thought about tying up the wound with a sheet as the blood washed over her hands and his together in rhythm. His face was all round black holes, staring up at her. The dark blood rushed out of him, staining her bed. She was covered in it. Her knife had fallen to the floor. She thought about her phone, realizing she had knocked it across the room when she'd sent the nightstand tipping over. Then she remembered it was useless.

She looked back at him, and the coursing of blood was getting weaker. His arms were growing slack and his choking sounds were fading. She pushed harder against the wound and remembered how he had held her down, just like this.

It was over quickly. His hands relaxed and slid away from his neck. She let go when he did, watched him go limp all over. She saw the gap in his throat, a ragged trench that leaked out slow blackness.

Her feet tangled when she tried to get out of the bed and she fell out of it instead. She tried to stand and her knee found her still-open knife on the floor. It made a tiny cut in her skin and she mechanically walked into the bathroom and found the peroxide in the cabinet by feel. She opened the white cap of the brown bottle and poured it out over the tiny cut in her knee until the bottle was empty. The bubbling, cold liquid ran down her leg on to the tile floor.

"Blood borne pathogens," she said in a completely neutral tone of voice.

She found another bottle under the sink, casually knocking unwanted things out on to the floor. When she found it, she opened it and upended it over her chest. She had forgotten the tamper seal, and nothing came out.

"Oh." She pinched the plastic half-circle with her right hand and pulled. Peroxide poured out and she ran it over her arms and neck, washing blood off her body. She poured it over her panties, soaking the crotch. It puddled pink and foaming on the floor. It soaked the carpet at the bathroom door. When she was finished, she put the cap back on the bottle and dropped it neatly into the bathroom trash.

Cold and dazed, she walked back out into her bedroom and tried not to look at the body. She slipped into a pair of jeans she found draped over a chair. She threw the wet shirt she had been wearing on the floor and pulled another from her closet. She put on a hoodie over it, then found a pair of socks and tied up her shoes. She walked back to her bed and pulled the sheet over the face she had never really seen.

Her hands found her cellphone on the floor and slipped it into the tight back pocket of her jeans. She closed her knife carefully and slipped it into a front pocket. She picked up her journal out of the wreck of her nightstand and shoved it down the front of her hoodie. She locked the door to her apartment and left with nothing in her hands.

The lone woman walked out onto the street and saw the orangey-pink in the east that meant the sun would rise soon. She walked up and down the hilly streets of San Francisco, not precisely in herself and not thinking. She came to a place she knew. It was a café she had come to a few times. She walked in, numb and cold, and sat on an old leather couch.

There was no one on the streets to hear her wailing. She sobbed and shook so hard she thought she would break. Her head throbbed and her throat ached and she pounded herself in the chest with both fists. She held her face and screamed and asked questions with no answers. She begged and apologized and raged.

When there was nothing left to say, she got quiet and pushed herself into the corner of the couch. She pulled her legs up close to her, knees tight together. She wrapped her arms around herself and pulled the hood over her face. She thought she might fall asleep, but she watched the sun rise, husked-out and raw. When it was full light, she got up stiffly and walked out the door.

She wandered into the Mission District without any idea where she was headed. The sidewalks were covered with broken glass and garbage, single shoes and the usual piles of city junk. In the street, cars were parked neatly in some places and rose up on the sidewalks in others. The road was choked here and there with accidents both minor and severe. She saw that some of the wrecked cars had corpses in them, including one pinned to a motorcycle trapped between two small cars. She tried to stop looking after that.

The Mission was always dirty, it was always derelict, but it had formerly been teeming with life. Alarming and empty now. The windows of the stores and restaurants were broken and there was no movement. Above the stores, windows to flats were hung with blankets and flags rather than curtains, looking as unkempt as ever but deadly silent. The only thing she could hear in the cold morning air was the flapping and cooing of pigeons, with the occasional shrill seagull. The city was without streetcars or hordes of people, without dogs barking or music pouring out of windows and the small radios carried by the homeless.

She smelled the sea and the sweet odor of rot from both food and dead bodies all around. The corners and alleys smelled like piss, maybe they always would. Block after block went by and she hesitated, thinking of traffic and signals and safety. She had to force herself to stop worrying about being hit by a car and start thinking what she should do if she saw another person. This was the first walk she had ever taken in this neighborhood that had not brought with it the smell of a dozen people smoking weed, the haze drifting from windows and bold passerby. Her senses were ringing the bell; the city was dead.

A different smell was beckoning to her. As she came to a corner, she could hear a little noise and she hid in the eave of a theatre, under the marquis, listening. Somewhere on the other side of the intersection, someone was cooking. And singing.

She stayed there as the smell grew stronger. She could smell garlic and mushrooms, she was sure. She heard the singing only in snatches, but the voice sounded high. She thought she should turn around and go the other way, and she fought with herself on that for a long time. In the end, hunger and simple curiosity won out. She came out cautiously and walked into the intersection. With a glance in all directions, she crossed diagonally away from a liquor store that stank like someone had smashed every bottle inside. The wind shifted and the aroma came again. Garlic and corn and cheese. Her stomach growled.

She came to the busted-out windows of an old Mexican restaurant with faded signs. The door stood open. She didn't see anyone. She walked through, craning her neck toward the sound. The song was clearer now; it was old with lyrics in Spanish. The person singing was doing a pretty good impression of the dead singer. She came through a short door into the kitchen.

A tall dark-skinned man stood at a gas grill, cooking an assortment of pupusas and sweating. He turned toward her with a smile, then goggled at her with his mouth open.

"Who the hell are you?" His accent made the last word joo.

"I'm… I'm… that smells amazing. I didn't mean to bust in on you. Are you…?" She stood half in the doorway, deciding whether to run. She didn't know what she should ask. Are you dangerous?

Are you gonna eat that? Terror and curiosity fought hunger and disorientation. She stood, unable to obey any of them.

He put the spatula down slowly. "Look, I just wanted to make some food. I don't want any trouble. I'm waiting for my friend, Chicken. If this is your place, I'm sorry."

"No, no it's not my place. I'm from across town. I haven't seen anybody else on the street."

"You and me both, girl. Me and Chicken thought we were the last two motherfuckers on earth."

She watched him closely. She knew he was gay. It was in everything, the way he stood in a long curve with his hips forward at the stove, the way he held his mouth when he called her 'girl.' It was in his delicate but deft hand as he flipped the pupusas. It was in the way he didn't look her up and down or linger anywhere but her face. She knew and she knew him immediately. It was a snap judgment to make, but she had lived and worked with gay men in San Francisco her whole life. Most of her best friends had been gay men, especially since after twenty-five most of her female friends had disappeared down the rabbit hole of marriage and come out mothers on the other side. She relaxed a little and came all the way through the door.

"You don't look like a looter," he told her, turning his attention back to the food.

"I'm not. I was sick with whatever the fuck everyone had and woke up at UCSF. Where did everybody go?"

"You were at UCSF, you tell me. The news said everyone was dying, especially the ladies. Some pundit asshole was saying it was an extinction event and all the women would die."

She leaned against the wall, staring at the food. "It was really contagious. Airborne. It appeared everywhere at once. I knew it was deadly, but there is nobody anywhere. I can't get over it."

He switched the gas off and piled pupusas on to paper plates. The plates were the cheap kind, so he stacked up four or five to support the weight of the food. "I'm Joe. My friend Chicken is out getting us water. The water is off everywhere. I can't believe the fucking gas is still on." He carried the plates out into the dining room and swept glass and balled-up napkins off the table.

"Might as well sit down, have something to eat."

She sat opposite him in one of the mismatched chairs. "I'm Karen," she said as she moved pupusas on to her plate with a plastic fork. He hadn't offered his hand and neither did she. He went back to the kitchen and came back with four different kinds of hot sauce.

They skipped the rest of the introduction because they both wanted to eat. She was starving, her mouth flooding at the sight of hot food on her plate. She shoveled in huge bites, the melted cheese scalding the roof of her mouth.

She was not Karen. Karen had died a week ago, still wearing her nametag. He wasn't going to ask for ID. She decided to be Karen for now.

He poured out dots of bright red sauce on to his own pile of food and shoveled just as fast. When they'd both finished a plate full, they slowed down. She took one more, he took two.

She poured green sauce over the pancake-like pupusa in front of her. "I can't believe this is all still good. All the fresh food I had had gone bad. I think I was at the hospital for ten days, maybe more."

He talked with his mouth full, but held his right hand in front of his face as he spoke. "Almost everything here was bad. All the meat was rotten and most of the cheese. I used to work here. There's an old icebox they store the mushrooms and onions and garlic in and it seals tight. I thought it might be ok, but there was wrapped up masa and some cheese in there, too. Still good, 'cause the cheese is dry. It's my lucky day. I knew the gas was on, 'cause we passed a couple gas leaks over on Van Ness."

"My lucky day, too. I'm alive." It hurt to swallow, but she meant it.

There was a sound of commotion in the back of the kitchen, and Joe popped up out of his chair.

"Chicken?"

"Joe, help me! I got caught!"

Joe ran to the back and Karen followed. Chicken turned out to be a tall scared-looking black kid, no more than twenty years old. His eyes were huge and rolling and his broad hands seemed to be holding him up in the doorway. His left leg was wrapped in razor wire. It wound in and out of his jeans and the denim was purple with blood in a couple of places.

"Shit," Joe said as he stared.

Karen pushed him out of the way. She put her shoulder against Chicken's body and pulled his long muscular arm over her shoulder. Together, they hobbled out of the kitchen out into the dining room. She helped him ease down onto the counter and pull his legs up after him. He reached for his injured leg and she caught his hands.

"Don't pull, you might make it worse. Let me help you."

"You a nurse? Who is this chick, Joe?"

"Karen. She just showed up."

"I am a nurse, I worked at the medical center. I can help you." She turned to Joe. "There's a drug store on this block, isn't there?"

He looked out the door, unsure. "I think so?"

She looked back at Chicken. "Is it safe to go out?"

"Nobody is after me." He gritted his teeth and looked at his leg.

"Ok. Joe, run to that drug store, and I mean run. Bring me back peroxide, in the brown bottle. You know that, right?"

"I know what peroxide is, Jesus." He looked more annoyed than scared.

"Okay, peroxide and gauze and an ace bandage. Go quick."

He was out the door without another word.

She pulled her knife out of her pocket and opened without looking at it. She couldn't remember if she had cleaned it or not. She decided it didn't matter and started cutting at Chicken's jeans. She thought to try to cut the wire out but realized it was a waste and cut the jeans around below the knee. She pulled at the hem and watched him. If the razor wire was caught in his skin, any movement would make him jump. He didn't, so she pulled straight down.

There was a lot of blood, but the damage wasn't that bad. He had a few deep cuts in the belly of his calf and one spot in his shin with a long slice of skin taken off, still hanging by a shred at the bottom. She pulled at it decisively and it popped off. Chicken yelped.

"Sorry, something was stuck to you." In her experience, it was always better not to say that skin was what had been ripped off. "Where were you?"

"I was up in some apartments like a mile away. I was looking for water."

She pulled his bloody sock and shoe off. "Joe told me. So what happened?"

"I was in this building with a bunch of flats and I was checking each one for bottled water. I got to this one in the middle and the door was open. I went straight for the kitchen and I found some glass bottles of Pellegrino and I started to load them up. This guy came screaming out of the bedroom. He covered in blood and looking real fucked up. He was holding like a shovel or like a little spade or something, I don't know what it was but he scared the everfucking shit out of me. He block the door so I went out the window. I was hanging off a window ac, trying to drop to the awning underneath. I missed and hit the windowsill and got tangled up in this shit here. I roll down the awning and hit the ground running. Fucking like going to the gym in hell. Ran all the way back."

Joe came pounding back in the door. "Here, I got it I got it I got it." He swung a plastic shopping bag on to the counter where it banged. She pulled the peroxide out of it and opened it up.

"He's ok, Joe," she said evenly. It looks bad but most of the cuts are superficial. As long as it doesn't get infected, he'll be ok." She poured peroxide over the skinned chunk of shin and he screeched through clenched teeth. Joe came around and grabbed his hand.

"I know it stings, I know." She poured more over his leg, pushing the calf muscle to one side to make the cuts gap open and poured again. "Just remember, that sting is the shit that wants to kill you dying off. The sting is good. The sting will save you."

Chicken gripped Joe's hand tight.

"So you didn't get any water?"

"No I didn't get any water, bitch. I got back alive. Fuck."

"Ok, sorry. Just checking. We'll get some."

"I want some new jeans, too. And shoes. And FUCK that hurts."

"I know, I know. Almost done." She flushed the cuts again and opened a package of gauze and used it to blot the wounds. Then she unrolled another and started to wrap it tight enough to hold but not too tight to walk in. When it was done up, she wrapped again with the ace bandage and used the tiny teeth in the closure butterflies to hold the whole thing together.

Chicken swung his legs off the counter. "Girl, you better be ready to feed me." Karen stiffened but Joe ran to the table and brought back a stack of cooled pupusas and a bottle of hot sauce. Chicken held it in his lap and started to eat.

They stood around while he ate. Joe watched Chicken. Karen

stared out the front door, thinking.

Chicken finished and set his plate aside. "Thank you, baby." He snaked his neck around and kissed Joe on the cheek. Joe smiled. "We need to find a place with water and stay there for the night. And get some clothes. You coming?"

They both looked at her.

"Sure," she said. She was better off with them than on her own, she decided. "Take it easy on that leg," she said to Chicken. "We can walk slow."

He rolled his eyes and hopped off the counter, then winced. "Ok," he said warily. "We go slow for now."

They walked at his pace, away from the direction that Karen had come. They checked out the drugstore Joe had been in and had a soda each, but the water was gone. They tried a boba shop and a row of restaurants. Syrups and toppings, bottles of ketchup and soy sauce. No water. By noon the fog had cleared and they were very thirsty.

"How the hell is there no water anywhere?" She was starting to feel crabby.

"The panic," Joe said simply.

"The panic?"

"Yeah," Chicken broke in. "Bad news freak people out, they panicking. They at the store, buying up toilet paper and water and guns, except they hardly any guns in San Francisco. Since the water been off, we been looking for water. Every day."

She tried to do the math. How many days in the hospital? How many days sick and unconscious? How many days until the city fell into panic? How long since the power and water died? The last day she could remember waking up in her apartment with lights on, catching the bus, and going to work was back in January.

"What's today?"

"Huh?" Joe looked at her like she was crazy.

"Do you guys know what today is? Like the date?"

Chicken snorted. "You gotta be somewhere? Come on, let's try in here."

They were at the door of an office building. The front door stood slightly ajar.

"Why here?" she asked.

"I got an idea."

They went up the stairs, which were windowless and dark. They came out on to the second floor into a huge room full of cubicles. Sunlight flooded in from the glass walls. Chicken went to one end of the room, Joe and Karen followed his lead and spread out. Karen looked at desks she passed, hoping for a water bottle at a workstation. She saw dead plants hanging over the sides of their pots and pictures of children. She came to a dead end. From the other side, she heard Joe yelling.

"I got it!"

She jogged in the direction of his voice. Joe stood beside the office bathrooms. Standing between them was a nearly full water cooler, with a fat, upright blue five-gallon bottle. Joe had sunk to the floor and was filling a paper cup. Karen grabbed one right after him and got out of Chicken's way when he hobbled around the nearest cubicle. They sat and drank cup after cup.

"Why are you called Chicken?" she asked when the silence had gone too long.

"I won a game once," he said.

"A game of chicken?"

"Yeah." He stared into his cup.

"Did the other guy die?"

His head snapped up. "No! He swerve out the way. I won his car. Did that a couple times and sold the cars. Made some money that way."

"Oh. What did you do for a living, Joe?"

"Mostly I worked in restaurants. Cooking and cleaning type of shit. Sometimes I worked lights in theaters for shows. That's where I met Chicken."

"Yeah, I ran soundboards. We been dating like maybe three months before all the theaters were closed. Shit, I was pissed. But everybody was too sick to go on anyway."

She remembered the theaters closing about a month ago. A temporary measure, the city said, to combat the worst flu season on record. It was hard to think that she hadn't seen it coming then, but no one had.

"Have you guys seen many people since the panic died down? Besides shovel-man?"

"Some," Joe said. "Seems like everybody died or left the city. But everybody is like, crazy."

Chicken was nodding. "Every motherfucker got a gun or some shit. Everybody either act like they wanna kill you, or you gonna kill them. I couldn't believe Joe let you in." He wasn't smiling.

"Yeah, but..." Joe looked guilty.

"Yeah but what," she pressed him.

"I haven't seen no girls. No women. No ladies. Cero mujeres. You the first woman I seen alive since I left my mama, and I know she was dying. I left her in Sac while I could still get home. I needed to find Chicken." He leaned his head on Chicken's shoulder.

"Are you guys going to stay in the city? Keep searching for water?"

Chicken shrugged and Joe got off him. "Why not? It's our city. It's mostly empty. Maybe we get a big house and all the water and food in the world."

"Then what?"

"What do you mean?" Chicken looked at her blankly.

"No other people. No kids. No work to do. Just, what? Surviving?"

Chicken laughed a little and filled up another cup. "We don't need other people. We were never gonna have kids. Living is work enough. And all we've ever done is survive. It might look different if you go to college and buy a house and do all that shit, but all we do is survive. Ain't nothing changed. Just now there's less competition." He drained his cup.

She nodded. Yes, that's true. No it isn't. Wasn't. Won't be. Won't be enough. Could I stay here? With them, or near them? Stay home, Jack might find me.

They fell asleep as soon as the sun started to set, curled up on the hard office carpeting, their bellies sloshing and full of water.

In the morning, they climbed to the next floor. One office had a kitchen full of shelf-stable snacks, all bright colors and preservatives. They ate these for breakfast and drank half the contents of another water cooler.

Even without working plumbing, they all felt compelled to use the bathrooms for their intended purpose. Karen sat in a stall with the weak diffused light from the open door slanting in under the stall dividers and pooling around her feet. She thought she'd never have to stand in line to do this again, and the feeling was emptiness.

Clumsily, they filled empty juice bottles and a handful of thermoses with the clean water from the cooler and left the office building in the afternoon. They all needed a change of clothes but couldn't decide where to go.

"There's a mall like ten blocks that way. We can just follow the tracks," Karen said, pointing.

"There's all the Chinese knockoff stores like right here," said Joe, pointing away.

"Yeah but they might not have everything we need."

"They'll have everything we need," Chicken said.

There's me and there's them. Don't need them, but still…

"Fine," Karen said turning away. "Guess we can meet-"

The explosion knocked them all flat down. Chicken had fallen almost on his face and came up with his lips bloody. Joe was scratched up and down both arms from grinding against the pavement. Karen pushed up on her palms and felt the wave of heat on her face.

Joe was screaming but she heard nothing but a high-pitched whine.

"THE FUCKING GAS!" He was screaming it over and over, but she had to read his lips to know it. Chicken grabbed Joe and ran, pulling him along, stumbling in huge strides away from the blast.

Karen looked back over her shoulder and saw a wall of flame covering one of the buildings facing her, with gouts of fire spilling out of the lower windows where gas must have pooled before a spark ignited it. She scrambled up and ran after the men, grabbing her water bottle at the last second. She found them sheltering on the cool side of a shaded brick building. She leaned her back against the wall and drank long and deep from her bottle. When she brought it back down, she could see they were trying to talk but nobody could hear. Gesturing gave way to scratching the brick surface of the wall with a pebble.

They argued whether they were safer indoors or outdoors, whether to head for the waterfront or continue north of the peninsula. Chicken wrote out that GAS STINKS twice and then underlined it. He was sure they'd be safe if they didn't smell it. But they hadn't smelled it back in the street.

Karen scratched out INSIDE BETTER and then MALL??

PROB NO GAS IN MALL.

They shrugged and followed her. They walked the whole way deaf and shell-shocked, unable to hear one another.

The mall had been boarded up against looters, but the boards had been pulled loose by someone before them. It was lit inside by the skylights, but the light didn't reach into the stores. They split up to find clothes, frustrated and tired of screaming and gesturing at each other.

DON'T GET LOST, Joe scratched into a movie poster on the wall. She gave him a thumbs-up and walked away.

Karen got a sturdy backpack at a store that sold clothes for teenage girls. She passed by the mannequins with their high, small breasts and exposed stretches of belly and thigh and felt a pang of something. Loss or disappointment, she couldn't tell. She left that store and headed to another. None of the women's clothes she looked at seemed durable enough. She didn't care how she looked, she just wanted clean clothes that would stand up to what she would have to do. She thought back to her stack of scrubs, always ready to go, but they weren't for all terrain travel, either. She loaded up wads of clean underwear in her size and got a couple of sports bras. She put one on and stuck the rest in the bag. She hadn't had a bra on in days and she welcomed the feeling of containment and protection.

She ended up at a store for young men and found pants and shirts that fit. She put her own hoodie back on, then decided against it and pulled a thicker one off a wall display. She sat down and brushed out her hair at the accessories table before braiding it into a long plait that hung down her back. She had always worn her hair in braids at work, so much that when work friends saw her at a party she knew they'd be shocked to see it down. It was long and dark and always wavy, curly on a humid day. She pulled on a baseball cap and threaded her braid through the space above the snaps in the back. She looked in the mirror and cringed a little.

Her reflection looked alarmingly tired. Her collarbones stood up and the skin under her eyes looked too thin. She touched the spot where she'd been punched, thinking it looked a little puffy. It was sore, but not bruised. She hadn't had makeup on in a long time and she was shocked at how unfeminine she appeared. Dehydration showed itself in her lips and she stuffed a pocket full of chapstick at the counter. The thing that bothered her most was her eyes. Her small brown eyes, where she always believed people could see who she really was if they looked close enough. They looked afraid. She looked pale, sick, hurt, and afraid. She squared her shoulders and stood up straight. She watched her reflection do it, and she tried a smile. It didn't come together the way it should have. She looked like prey, like a mark. She'd seen that look before on women who came to the ER, bleeding from one end or the other. Nobody chooses to be a victim, but after a lifetime of practice it just happens. She wanted that look off her, now. She'd have to work on it. For a half a second, she thought of her daily professional look; a quick dash of mascara and concealer, but she couldn't face the absurdity of it. She applied a thick coat of chapstick, working it in, stretching her lips over her teeth to crack the dry places and let the moisture in.

She came out feeling better, slinging the pack over her shoulder. She walked down toward the end of the building and saw there was a Starbucks near the boarded-up door. As she walked toward it, she tried snapping her fingers beside her ears. The right side heard nothing, but the left picked up the snap as though it was happening under water. She hoped the damage was temporary.

The coffee shop cold case was all but untouched. She sat down and drank a whole bottle of water and one of the shelf-stable coffee drinks. It was room temperature, but tasted great to her. They hadn't agreed on a place to meet up again so she waited. When a little time had passed, she loaded up all of the fruit and nut bars and cookies from the register in her bag, took all the water and another coffee and started back. She stopped at the central staircase and looked around. She was thinking about loading her bag with the basics for first aid when she saw them.

Out of the corner of her eye, they might have been Joe and Chicken. She turned to look and saw they were four instead of two. She froze when they spotted her. One of them pointed at her and got the attention of the man next to him by swatting him backhanded on the chest. She couldn't hear a word, but their mouths were moving. One of them dropped a length of chain he had coiled around his hand. They broke into a run headed straight toward her.

She didn't understand what she was seeing, but instinct made her run. She was on the bottom level of the mall where the doors lead into the subway. The ground was two floors up. She took the spiral stairs two and three at a time, not stopping to look back. At the third level, she tore around a kiosk toward the door. She knew she'd have to stop to claw her way out past the boards. She looked over her shoulder and saw Joe and Chicken just steps behind. She half-heard them screaming, "GO! GO!"

She thumped the plywood with her shoulder twice before the nails popped out. The three of them slid through and the other four men followed. They ran around the corner together and Chicken flipped open a dumpster. Joe and Karen jumped in and Chicken followed nimbly, pulling the lid down on them. They waited.

Trying to breathe silently without being able to hear yourself is impossible. Karen stifled the urge to wipe the sweat off her face or change her position at all. Chicken held on to Joe with both hands, as if to hold him still. Joe held his own mouth.

They crouched there, not daring to move, for a long time. Chicken finally came up a tiny bit, pushing the lid of the dumpster with his head. He turned his neck slowly, checking both directions. Finally he stood up and flung the lid back.

"They gone. They ain't nobody out here." They couldn't hear him, but they saw it in his shoulder dropping down.

Joe trembled all over from the adrenaline. When he stood up his knees creaked. He came out and stood beside Chicken. Karen climbed out on her own.

"What in the hell was that all about," she bellowed toward

them, raising both hands and looking bewildered.

Chicken's head swiveled around to face her, ugly with rage. "That was about YOU. They wanted YOU. They saw you a girl and they decided they want to take you with them, so they run you down. We heard the noise and came running out and they decided we're defending you, so they gonna kill us. We don't need this shit."

"What? What are you talking about?"

Joe started to speak, but Chicken cut him off. "Fucking gas explodes whatever, that ain't your fault. And it ain't your fault you a female. But you are gonna make trouble for us, and we don't need you. I seen this shit coming when I seen no women. We ain't gonna die defending you. You gotta go."

"Look, I can defend myself. You won't have to-"

"Those guys would have acted tough, maybe made us leave the mall. They would have had no fight if they didn't see you. You too rare. We can't do this. I'm sorry. You gotta go. We gotta go. This ain't gonna work."

Only just met them so how can they break my heart? How does this ache like an abandoned child?

"Chicken, I probably saved your life. If that cut had gotten infected—"

"And we probably saved yours. We're even." He was already turning away.

Joe shrugged in that way that meant it wasn't up to him. He turned with Chicken's arm around his neck and they walked away.

Alone, she looked around in every direction and there was no reason to go in any of them. No one waited at the end of any road, no purpose or burden came with any choice. It was like falling through something with no bottom.

In the end, she picked a street and started to walk. She strained her ringing ears to hear anyone coming behind her, but she looked over her shoulder every few paces. She thought about how Joe and Chicken had looked in their clothes, and how she looked different. Simple differences, small changes. It was the beginning of a plan.

# Chapter Two

*1 May*

Have no idea of the date. Just sat here with this thing trying to guess for a couple minutes before I decided to say fuck it. Pretty sure it's May. It's been cold but the flowers are out. It isn't hot yet. More fog than before. Declaring it May.

Living in the basement of a rickety house on Capp St. Been here since the fires spread across the Mission. Have my kit, my knife, and a good stockpile of canned food. Raiding is pure hell and I'm sure I'll die doing it. Most of what I have I found in other houses. Found a revolver in a closet two days ago. At least it's a gun I know how to use. Took it apart, cleaned it up, spent some time getting used to the feel of it. Familiar. Friendly. Can stand searching houses and offices. After the mall, stores are too much, too open, with too many places to hide.

Made it back to the hospital, tried to find Jack or some sign of him. Been a year and everything = dry = crypt = fuck that. Nothing. Went back to the apartment, couldn't go in. Must have thought I was dying. Can't blame him. Left a note anyway. Time stopped a long time ago. Time was never time at all. Digital clocks gone blank.

No one to talk to now, long time. Last woman on earth. Going to go crazy if I don't talk to somebody besides myself. This = that. Substitution. Sham.

So, the bag. Journal, all the way in the bottom and flat. Food and bottled water. Inside my kit: army medic set for wounds, all the disinfectants and antibiotics I have left. Two topicals. Replace those pretty easy. 86 vials of Depo-Provera and a box of hypos. Two stashes of the patch. Three large boxes of the ring. All that = main pocket. Outside pockets: all the OB tampons I have left, two flashlights, twelve batteries, four lighters, and the map= enough to make camp in the East Bay and keep moving.

Don't know if it's any better on that side. Saw the fires in the Oakland hills, raging with nothing to stop them until the rains came. Up towards Berkeley things seemed a little better. Maybe head toward the university and raid there. Then move on. North. All the talk overheard sounds like heading south = go north.

Small group yesterday, close enough for me to wake up and hear them. Panicked at first, thinking they were in the house. Passing between houses, and they eventually stopped in one across the street. Got a hold of myself, heard them talking outside.

"...down toward San Diego. I heard it wasn't as bad in Mexico. Maybe we could live on the beach in Baja and go fishing."

"Man I guess. We need to find a car though. I'm fucking sick of walking. Maybe on the 101 we can find something that still runs."

A third voice laughed. "Even if it runs, there's nowhere to go with it. Everything is blocked. We could grab some motorcycles, maybe. But we'd need five."

"Four. She can ride bitch."

Small laughter. Listened to their steps leading away, my heart still pounding. Four men, then. One woman. Stayed in the locker with the garden tools until heard nothing at all for a long time. Neighborhood = nothing but ghosts for weeks, but time to move on. People moving down the peninsula, and there's no way no how no reason to get caught on a bridge. Heading down to the marina, steal a boat. Still sailboats, made sure. Everything that ran on gas is gone = not raiding for gas even if they aren't. Never sailed before, but it isn't far. Go tomorrow or the next day. Go tomorrow. Go during the night. Must gtfo. Go.

Bitch, call everyone bitch. Ride bitch, feed me bitch. Pussy=pussy. Choose the rougher word. Posturing. Easy laugh. Take it easy. Only joking. Bitch.

*June*

Getting out of the city took longer than I thought. Couple of weeks in indecision, not wanting to leave the basement. Ate everything I could, slept forever always in daylight. Hearing =mostly back, don't know if my right ear will ever be as good as it was. Packed and unpacked. Hated every day and chickened out every night. Pussy = pussy. Finally ran for it the night I heard the motorcycle. New one, rice-rocket. Ripped up and down the streets in the predawn hours. Felt like dragging my nerves out with it. Got too far away to hear anymore, figured that was it. Strapped on the knife and the gun, put on my pack. Walk.

Did an okay job of changing my look. I'm tall. Apartment in the Mission, found a compression vest to hide my tits. Thanks transman of yesteryear. Little too small, real tight. Shaved my head. Wasn't easy. Got men's cargo pants and combat boots, with a couple of loose shirts and my hoodie on top. Can't do anything about a beard. Couldn't find one in a costume shop or anywhere. Settled for rubbing dirt into my jaw every morning. Candlelit mirror tricky tricky. Look like a young effeminate man. A guy like Joe. Need to do more pushups.

Walk tall, keep hips straight. Don't sway. Feet flat. Hunch a little, arms straight down. Don't gesture. Stare down. Make fists while talking. Sit with knees apart. Adjust. Don't tilt your head. Don't bite your lip. Interrupt. Laugh low.

* * * * *

She found a sailboat that wasn't wrecked or hopelessly entangled after walking the marina until well after dawn. She felt horribly exposed, being out in the wide open. She thought it would be better than on a bridge, because she wouldn't have to choose to jump. The boat's name was Circe and that sounded like something bad but she couldn't place it. She looked all over at it to make sure there was only rope holding it down. She loosed the mooring and climbed aboard to push off the dock with a long pole. The tide started to drag her out. It was really working.

Hot damn. This might work. Maybe I'll get the hang of this and sail up the coast.

The feeling lasted a few minutes before it became clear that she didn't know how to sail. She turned a crank experimentally and was excited to see that it raised a sail. It caught the wind and dragged the ship backwards. Cursing, she raised another by pulley and it flapped uselessly, not made fast. She was almost chopped in half by one swinging arm and she worked, straining, to tie it down to something. She forgot that boats had rudders until she was out in the middle of the Bay, drifting without aim. When she found the tiller, she tried to turn it toward the east. That worked until the wind died. She began to seriously consider whether she could swim the rest of the way. The boat passed under the Richmond Bridge, following some current and running parallel to the shoreline. Lost at sea.

She heard the high choppy whine of a motor.

She whipped around to see a little boat coming toward her, running fast with a small outboard motor. There was only one man in it. She tensed all over.

He came alongside. "Hey, where you gonna take that thing?"

She shrugged, and pitched her voice as low as she knew how. "Just crossing the Bay, man."

"You could have walked the tunnel. Why get all this going?"

She had thought about walking through the BART tunnel. The idea of getting lost in there was more than she could handle. She looked him over as his boat came under her gaze. He was slight and clean-looking. His hands on the oars were long and slender with elegant fingers. He wasn't threatening. Not even trying.

"I thought it'd be easy. It's fine. I'll work it out."

"You wanna just climb down and I'll take you across?"

"I don't have anything to trade." If he tried to come aboard, she decided she'd push him overboard. Simple. Let him work that out while she got away.

The smell of salt came off the warmed surface of the water, but the wind cut cold and right through them. She did not want to swim.

"Nah, it's cool. I haven't seen anybody in a couple of days. I just miss people."

After a few seconds of thought, she decided if she had to get rid of him, she might as well be in the better boat. She decided it was too risky to throw her pack, so she came awkwardly down the ladder with it. The boat rocked alarmingly and she sat down fast, trying to keep it steady.

He held out his hand. "Curtis."

She shook with the best grip she could muster. "Andrew. Where are you headed?"

Curtis sat back and started the motor again, and the small boat resumed skipping toward the shore. "I dunno. Everybody left the city. Downtown is full of dead people. Where is there to go?"

"I'm going south, toward San Diego," she lied. "I heard it's not so bad down there, plus there's nice beaches."

"Yeah. That sounds pretty good." Curtis smiled that needy smile.

Harmless.

She turned her face into the wind and Oakland got bigger and bigger, black and wrecked on the coastline.

"Hey can we hook north toward the Berkeley marina? Oakland looks like shit from here."

"Sure." He turned the boat north. "So, what'd you do? Before."

Without thinking, she answered the way she always had. "I'm a nurse."

"No kidding! I didn't think I'd ever meet a nurse again."

"Yeah, well. Trauma. I was a field medic in Afghanistan before that." She came up with that in the white panic of exposure. She was impressed with herself.

"Oh, cool. If you find some people, at least you can tell them you're useful. I wrote code for Facebook, so once I eat all the baked beans in San Francisco, it's pretty much over for me."

She looked at his fake brave face. He was really trying, but underneath he was all terror. "People adapt," she told him.

"We'll see if I do. Is that what you're looking for? People?"

She shrugged. "Not sure I should."

He sat silent. She took that to mean he couldn't argue with her.

After a minute, he squeaked it out. "Well… well, can I go with you? Two are better than one. I can at least be a lookout and help you find food. I'm good with machines and directions. What do you say?"

Shit. Should have seen that coming.

She had been perfectly and calmly ready to ditch this guy and yet this question hurt her heart. She thought about Chicken telling her off. She couldn't look at him. Sideways, he looked like a little boy trying not to cry.

"I don't think that would work out. But you'll find some people. Good luck, okay?"

They were almost to the marina. She strapped her pack back on and he got close enough to a huge sailboat's ladder for her to grab on. She climbed up and looked back down at him.

"Ok then. I guess I'll go back."

Something gave way inside her. She turned her bag around and reached in for something she could give him, since she couldn't let him follow. "Here." She tossed down a rubber banded bundle of antibiotics. "Hold on to that. It might save your life."

He caught it and looked up. "Hey thanks. Good luck to you, too."

He took off. She couldn't explain to herself why she had given it to him. She had to give him something. She thought again of his long, slender hands and his innocent face. He was harmless. She could have helped him, adopted him, but she couldn't talk herself into the risk. She hoped he found somebody who would take him on. Save him.

Good luck, man.

She slept in the hold of a boat that had no food but about six kilos of weed. She sniffed its skunky, oily stink and thought about taking some. It might be good to trade, but it'd be a terrible idea to get stoned on her own. When it got dark, she decided she was sick of the smell and got out to walk up to the university. She looked back at the boat, knowing that she wouldn't return to it. She could set it on fire. She could burn down the whole marina. The night was clear and cool and the thought passed.

She had no flashlight, but there was an almost full moon. Most of downtown looked intact, and the school seemed to have held out for a long time when everything was falling apart. Dorms stood dark on every side, most with banners hanging out the window with slogans opposing the school closure and quarantine. One banner overhead read "3 INSIDE PLEASE HELP." She wondered if they were still there, or if help had come. Firelights flickered on an upper floor of an old brick pub and she crept away from it, around the block. She doubled back and came up to the main entrance of the school, and then hooked down the street. The building she was looking for was boarded up, but she picked at the edges of the plywood at one window until she found a way in.

*In Berkeley*

In the university clinic now. Been here a few days. Pallet of bottled water in here, plus cases and cases of granola bars and dried fruit. Also more birth control than I've seen anywhere else. Stocked up to bursting. Thousands of doses = all set.

*June*

Actually pulled it off. Wasn't sure it would ever work but I did it, today.

* * * * *

They were three, men and a woman. She was young. The midwife saw them coming around one of the old cafes, carrying boxes of cookies. It was broad daylight and she was prepared, right down to the socks in her underwear. She went out through the roof hatch and drew her gun.

Steady. You've got all the advantage. Stay steady. Ready? Talk low. Ready. Steady. Ready.

"Hey!"

They started and one of them men dropped his cookies. They both looked around wildly and froze when they saw her.

"Hey!" She started again, low and gruff. "Didn't mean to scare you. You interested in trade?"

"Fuck, dude," said the one with the black ponytail. "Don't pull a gun if you're not trying to be scary."

Maybe not next time. Maybe overcorrecting. Fuck it, I feel better with it showing.

"Just getting your attention. Trade?"

"Put that thing away and come down." They weren't showing any arms. She put the gun in the back of her waistband and climbed down through the hatch. She wiggled out of a back window where she couldn't be seen and came around the front, with her trade-goodie bag and her medkit. She came around showing her hands.

"My name's Rob. I'm holding some good stuff."

"I'm José, this is Mike and Jenna. What do you have?" José had the black ponytail, shiny with some kind of grease. Mike had a buzz cut and one arm was covered with tattoos.

"Well, I used to be a PA, so I can offer you medical assistance if you need it."

They looked at each other and back at her. "We're cool. You got more guns to trade?"

They didn't have one. "Nope, just mine. Not trading that."

"Damn. Okay, what else?"

"Liquor. Cigarettes. Candy. Good food. I'm a good raider. What do you want?"

José was quick to step up. "You got cigarettes? I seen no cigarettes anywhere in a long time. I'd kill for one."

"Regular, menthol, Black and Mild. You name it."

He licked his lips. "What you want for them?"

She looked down at them from under the bill of her ball cap, trying to look sly. "You know what I want. Is she your girlfriend? Or his?" She switched her gaze from José to Mike, not looking at Jenna.

They both looked at Jenna. She was about seventeen, with long dirty blonde hair grown out dark at the roots. She wore frayed jean shorts on long, tan legs and a loose blousy top. No bra. Her face wasn't bruised, but she never looked up.

"She's… uh…"

"Ok, I don't care. Point is, is she for sale?"

Mike jumped in this time. He was red haired with a scruffy beard, long ropy muscles with a lot of tattoos. She sized up his biceps and thought about her own skinny arms. "Yeah she is. But it'll cost you."

She stuffed her hands in her pockets, trying to close up her face while stealing glances at Jenna. The girl was not fazed by the discussion of her as an object. "Two packs of smokes, your choice. One bottle of the liquor I don't like."

I don't give a shit what they choose. Haggle anyway. Act like it matters. Keep looking at the girl.

José countered. "Four packs of smokes, one bottle each, our choice, and something to eat while you do her."

"Three packs. Two bottles, your choice. Two cans of pork and beans and you eat where I can see you."

They looked at each other, not talking.

"I need half an hour, man. That's all."

They turned back to her, grinning. "Ok, but you do it where we can see you."

She made a face. "No fucking way. I want some privacy. On the roof. You'll be able hear us."

Mike turned to José, who was clearly in charge. "What if he shoots her? Or throws her off the roof?"

"Why would I do that? I haven't seen a girl in months. And you two would figure out a way to kill me, gun or no gun. I'm not crazy. Just looking for trade. How about it?"

She told herself to stay relaxed, not to tense her shoulders or let her voice get high.

A young man is used to getting his way.

José nodded once. "Three packs. Two bottles. Food. Show it to us."

She slipped the small bag off her shoulder. She showed them the smokes and threw their choices at their feet. They picked one vodka and one whiskey. She set them down gently and lined up two cans of pork and beans beside them.

"Ok?"

"Mike, you got a can opener?"

"Right here, dude. Let's build a fire."

José pushed Jenna toward Rob without a word to the girl. "Don't fuck her up. I know you got a gun, but you were right when you said we'd kill you."

Rob reached out and put a hand on the back of Jenna's neck. She told the girl to go around the back of the building. She did, wordlessly obeying.

The young man turned back to them and winked. "Half an hour."

She turned and ran after the girl. She pushed her through the loose plywood slot and toward the ladder to the roof. Jenna broke through the hatch ahead of Rob and sat down on the white painted tar. Jenna drew her knees up to her chest and wouldn't look up. She dropped down beside her, unbuckling her med kit.

"How old are you?"

She didn't look up or speak.

"Jenna, we don't have much time. I'm not gonna fuck you. I'm trying to help. Look at me."

She wouldn't.

"Jenna. Jenna, seriously. Please try."

Nothing.

She picked up Jenna's hand and held it to her hairless jaw. "Look. See? I won't hurt you. Get it?"

She didn't.

She stood up and undid her belt. Jenna tensed all over, but wouldn't look.

"Look, goddamn it. Look!"

Frustrated, Rob threw the socks at the blonde and they bounced off her ankles. The girl looked up and saw the boxer briefs, empty in the front. "Look, see?" Rob went to pull the flap open and show her and her breath caught. It was too real, too much like she really was going to fuck her. Instead, she put her flat hand against her vulva and pulled it up tight. "No dick. Nothing. I'm a woman. See?"

Jenna looked up at Rob's face and began to cry.

Rob stuffed her socks back in and did up her pants, leaving the belt unbuckled. "Now, tell me. How old are you?"

"Seventeen. I was gonna be eighteen in October."

"How many times have you been pregnant?"

Her eyes were wide with terror. "Twice. Once when it was just José, and once since Mike."

"Did you give birth?"

"The last time, yeah. The first one I just bled out and got sick. In the winter. I had the baby like two months ago. He was dead."

Lucky she's alive at all. Don't tell her that.

"Ok. Ok, yeah. I know. Look, I'm gonna give you a shot. It'll keep you from getting pregnant again for almost two years. Then I'm gonna give you some little plastic rings. After the two years, you put them up inside you. They're only good for a month, then pull them out. If you get caught with them, say they're for dryness and you found them somewhere. Ok? Ok, Jenna?"

She was nodding while Rob dug out the Depo shot and sterilized the needle. Jenna cried out when she plunged it in and down on the street they heard laughing. She stuck a dozen of the tiny plastic rings in Jenna's jeans pocket.

She held her arm and looked up at Rob. "Have you seen any other girls?"

"Not a lot."

"Fuck."

"I can't get you away. I thought about it, but… Look, if you have a chance to get free, cut your hair. Dress like a boy. It doesn't always work, so-"

"I can leave anytime I want to. There's worse guys out there than José and Mike. They're alright."

"Ok. Sure. Yeah."

Rob didn't think their time was up yet. She heated up a can of pork and beans and watched Jenna wolf it down.

"You get to eat?" She cocked an eyebrow at the girl.

"Yeah. Just haven't had meat in a while. It's so fucking good."

She wiped her face and Rob mussed up her hair. Jenna got the idea and yanked her shirt up a bit. They came down disheveled and Rob grinned at them while she pushed the girl back into their midst.

"Good trade."

"He treat you ok, baby?" Mike murmured this into her hair. José stared at them both.

She nodded, looking down.

Rob showed them her hands again. "Like I said, just looking for trade. No harm done."

They had drunk a little of their booze, but not too much. She watched them pack up with her back leaning against the brick front of the clinic. There wasn't anything to say in summation. No information to exchange. No reason to say a warm goodbye or thanks. Slowly they moved off and she wiggled back into the building.

*****

Barely slept since then. Hate that they know where to find me. Hate that. Hate that. Should have tried to get her away. Sooner or later, though, one of them is going to kill the other to get Jenna alone. Should keep them busy.

Should have saved her. Me, Curtis, Jenna. Running together. Coulda shoulda woulda saved them both. Coward.

Have to move on. Keep moving.

Way he put his hand on the back of her neck. Way he smelled her while looking at me. Disregard, control. Shrug up a little, make shoulders bigger. Pluck at crotch of my jeans. Hard eye contact. Remember. Practice in front of a mirror. Find a mirror.

*July*

Hot as shit here. Somewhere near Sacramento, though I haven't gone into the capital. Heard gunshots from that direction, and it's lit up at night. No way. Nope nope nope.

*July*

Little Urgent Care that's been almost completely cleaned out. Somebody spray painted NO SUPPLIES out front- thanks. Exit in back and it's in a strip mall. Raiding here sucks. Convenience food mostly. All the jerky was gone when I got here. So sick of chips I could die. So salty all the time.

Started to head for the 5 freeway but 1: sure there are people on it 2: there's no water and no food along it hardly at all. Remember driving before, and even in an air conditioned car it seemed like a wasteland. Just gas stations and nothing. Roads east lead into the Nevada desert. No way not doing that this time of year. Hook north through Oregon and then Idaho, but it's all mountain passes. Take me forever, especially the back roads. No good plan.

Where the fuck am I going?

*August*

Haven't seen hardly anyone since Jenna. Haven't heard voices but some very distant sounds of others. Garbage along the road and old fires. That's it. Nobody no bodies.

*August*

Getting close to Oregon border? Found tiny lake = beautiful vacation houses lined up around it. Staked out for a day until thunderstorm hit. Just broke into one = gun in hand. Nobody.

First two had nothing, not even furniture. Third was fully stocked for a family with a lot of kids. Shut the flue, blocked most of the doors made a camp on the sofa backed up against the fireplace. Must have been a winter lodge for them. Closets are full of down comforters and parkas and big coats. Can outfit myself for heading north here.

Been here two weeks. There's a huge stash of baby food and I almost cried when I saw the strained peas. Fruits and vegetables. Been too long. Lot of canned soup with meat in it and plenty of dry goods. Putting some weight back on. Working out every day = build muscle = pass time. Full bookshelves. Classics popular novels some nonfiction. Some stuff I had on my list from way back but never had time. Like vacation, like a retreat. Could stay here forever. Boarded the windows with furniture pieces. Not great = better than nothing. Glass.

Rub jawline. Don't look down. Stand in front of the mirror. Have a dick. Great big dick. Fear me. Always right. Kick your ass.

No right to stand in my way. Who's gonna stop me? Like that, bitch? Yeah.

No candles except a bag of tea lights in a bathroom. Made do. Resisted the urge to start a fire and boil water for a bath in one of the huge tubs. Too easy for the smoke to get spotted. Too risky to be caught naked. Basic hygiene = water from the lake warmed up over a can of Sterno. That's it.

Debated how long I can stay here. Enough food for me to get through the winter, maybe. Sleeping pretty well here = keep my back to the wall and my gun in my hand. Maintain maintain find a spot and hold it make a stand.

*August maybe September?*

Still here. Thunderstorms are intense. Reinforced the windows with the bed slats from upstairs, but left slits to see through. Clouds slide over the lake and sink there like water pooling before a drain. Rains and rains and rains and rains, never hear anyone coming. Thinking about finding some bells or something and setting up trip wires, just to hear someone coming. Haven't seen or heard anyone in ages, though.

Not quite true. Raided one of the houses on the far side of the lake yesterday that turned out to be full of the dead. Must have fled the cities and died here. Maybe fifteen people, too decomposed for me to really tell but long hair = maybe women. Mostly died in bed. Place stays wet and the summer was warm = smell the stink from outside. Door was unlocked. Tied a bandana around my face and went in. Opened the curtains for light. Two of them were laid out on sofas, faces covered. Must have gone first. Loaded pack with the soup and canned fish from their cabinets, trying not to breathe through my nose.

Upstairs, found a little jar of Vicks and smeared it on my bandana for the smell. Went into my pocket never know when you might need Vicks=breathing. One bedroom, a dead guy in a flannel jacket sat propped up next to a dead woman in bed. Fancy nightgown and her jaw was wide open. Rosary beads in bed with her. Turned to the guy and gloved up. I searched his pockets and found a wad of cash, threw it on the floor. ID said he was from Las Vegas. Tried not to look at his name or his age. Didn't matter. Waistband=gun=jackpot=small semi-automatic pistol all but glued to what was left of his hand. Ripped it off and the sound was like tearing through the skin on a roast turkey. Got over that, found the box of bullets in his jacket pocket. Raid was worth it. Could make a huge difference.

Another room had three dead children. Two little boys and one older girl. Stood in the doorway long enough to name them.

John.

Michael.

Wendy.

Shut it. Nothing nothing and nothing in there I want.

Another long-haired corpse in a dry bathtub. Two more in another big bed, together. Ornate jewelry box in the corner and looked. Good stuff. Fingered the diamonds shinybright. Anyone trade for them? Decided no. Left it open full of treasure.

Last bedroom kept me for a while. Empty but= looked tossed and lived-in. Bed unmade drawers half empty. Completely empty box of chocolates sat on the floor, a good pair of heels. Searched the whole thing=nothing of value. On the bureau a letter in a sealed envelope next to pair of emerald earrings. Addressed to Tamara. Opened it.

LETTER FROM ANDREA TO TAMARA
THE YEAR OF THE DYING
AS SCRIBED BY THE UNNAMED MIDWIFE

Dear Tam,

I'm taking off. I feel so much better and I know I'll be ok. I tried to pack up everything useful, but who knows what I forgot. I am so sorry about the children, and about you and Dick. I really thought getting us out of Vegas was the answer. I guess I was wrong.

Please forgive me for not burying any of you. When Maryanne and Lucia died, we debated it. Ryan said he would help but in the end none of us could face it. I can't face it alone, I know that. We don't even have a shovel. I thought about burning the house down to take care of everybody, but it might take the whole lake and the woods. I'm going to leave you all as you are. I'm sorry.

You know I slept with Dick. It was years ago and we were so drunk and so stupid. I swear it never meant anything, it just happened. I'm so sorry I hurt you, and I hope you two are in heaven together and that you can forgive him. You might be able to forgive me soon, too.

I'm going to head south toward Mexico. Before the news stopped, they were saying it was better down there. I'll head straight down the 5, maybe steal a car. Wish me luck.

I don't know why I'm writing this. I had to say something. I was so sick that when I woke up I didn't know where I was. I found you dead and there was nothing I could do. I'm sorry.

Please forgive me. I love you both. I'll see you when I get to where you are.

Always,
Andrea

Balled it up and threw it on the floor. Andrea had gotten out. Wished her well.

Brought everything I found back here. Think I know how to use this gun. Found the safety and I can load the clip. Good to have another one. Wish I could practice with it.

* * * * *

On a clear day, she climbed the tallest hill to get a better sense of where she was. She saw Mt. Shasta in the distance and thought she could identify it on the map. She was close to Oregon, then. She could see small fires south of her, probably campfires. She heard nothing.

She took two practice shots with the new gun, aiming at a tree at a distance from the house. The gun popped like a toy and there was almost no recoil. Compared to her revolver, it barely felt real. It was light and accurate. She liked it, and fingered it constantly.

She came down on the other side of the hill to circle around to the lake. There was a bait and tackle store, she decided to check it out. She raided some chewing tobacco and gum. Signs hung askew and the cash register had been emptied. There was not much left inside but the bugs that had lived through it all, skittering over everything when the light fell upon them. She shivered, but looked anyway.

They had a couple of newspapers from last year. She glanced over the stories of "Lymphatic Fever" and "Women's Plague." There were awful pictures of hospitals in New York and Paris overflowing with the dead and dying. No cure in sight, ran one lede. Men recovering at ten times the rate of women, ran another. Nothing she didn't know, but she stared.

How did it get so out of hand? How did it spread so fast? Why did I recover?

Her hospital in San Francisco had a great lab. Everyone who had any lab tech experience had been locked up in there, looking at this thing under a microscope. She wasn't one of them, she worked in labor and delivery, trying to bring fevers down and watching women birth dead and dying babies. She recalled the pandemonium, when she tried to call it up and reason it out. She had never attended a stillbirth before. The first couple were solemn and chastened doctors struggled to explain dead babies patiently, compassionately. After a solid week of them and one hundred percent infant mortality, there was quarantine protocol and screaming, wailing, demanding answers. Parents and doctors alike were unhinged. She remembered putting a baby girl on a Japanese woman's chest. The child lived long enough to curl her hand around her mother's finger, and then she was gone. Limp and turning blue. They resuscitated, they injected, wheeled crash carts to every room. The girl's mother died that day, on fire with a fever they couldn't touch. Within hours, the baby's father disappeared.

No cure in sight and the lab crew thinned out. Hospital staff died and disappeared as panic overtook them and mayhem took the city. Dead nurses lined the halls with dead patients and after a while, nobody was hauling them out anymore. She remembered staying so busy that she didn't see what was happening until she couldn't open a door. When she finally got sick there was nobody to look after her. Only Jack had come, and she believed he had come to say goodbye.

She could not get the memory to come clear. Her heart pounded and she could relive the terror, but she couldn't tell the memory of one day in chaos from another. She could not sequence the events, or understand how something this sudden and final had come to be. She was sorry every time she looked back. She set herself up with tasks and focused on the present. Examining the timeline in any direction away from now profited her nothing.

September

Found a motorcycle. Really small, but in good shape. Boathouse=huge drum of gas. Covered it up with tarps. Hope it's still there when ready to leave. Had one of those shitty multipacks of cheap fireworks for the 4th of July. Took it with me, but bet most are duds by now. Hiss boom fuck you.

* * * * *

The party of men arrived on the lake one day before sunset.

They were startlingly loud in the continuous quiet. She crept to the window to see how many. She counted ten for sure, but they weren't still or close or easy to see. They settled into a house on the opposite side of the lake and fell to fishing and drinking. She knew they'd begin raiding the surrounding houses, just as she had done. She worried about possibilities in order: they would find her motorcycle, they would find her.

Two days passed and she watched the men ceaselessly, unable to sleep. Their constant drinking kept them slow and unambitious. Late on the third day, they finally started to venture around the lake. She had created a sniper's perch where she could see out and shoot straight but would be difficult to spot from the ground.

When they came around to her house, they tried the door and couldn't budge it. One of them picked up a rock to break a window and she took a deep breath and fired through her tiny slit in the window. She shot the ground beside him, but she could see his jeans darken where he pissed himself.

"This one's taken," she yelled down to them, gruffly. "We're armed, and we'll defend it. Fuck off."

Get calm. Panic sounds like panic and any dog can hear it. Breathe deep. Remember you have the advantage. No one has seen you.

A few of them stepped back. All their eyes looked up. It wasn't the whole party. She swept them in her sights. A few held weapons, one or two was swaying drunk.

One bearded face yelled up at her, she cringed at the sound of it. His voice was rough and low and slightly amused. "What have you got in there? Girls?"

She tried to change her voice to sound like another guy. "No girls. Just heroin. Lots of heroin. Fuck off." Shit, that sounded really stupid. I suck at this.

A couple of them laughed. "Fucking junkie."

The same one yelled up again. "We don't want your drugs, man. We're just looking for food and good stuff."

"You're not looking for it here," she yelled back down. "Looks like we have guns and you don't. We suggest you leave this lake."

They talked to each other, low. They didn't move off.

Please go please please please go and leave me alone.

She moved to the other window she had rigged and lit one of the strings of firecrackers she had found in the boathouse, praying that they were live. She tossed them overhand toward the men. They were live and utterly unexpected on the ground. Men jumped and flailed when the tiny crackers went off. A few ran back toward their camp, others took a long last look before following. She caught more than a few looking back and up at her. She took one more shot after them, just as a warning. Exhausted, she laid on the floor and slept until it was dark.

She woke up in perfect stillness and ate a jar of baby food bananas. She did some pushups and went back to her lookouts. There was no one outside. Across the lake, a fire burned in a pit. They had retreated but they had not left.

For a moment, she considered starting a fire in her own fireplace. She wasn't hiding anymore; they knew she was in there. Dismay set in as she realized that their smoke would draw more people to the lake.

She nodded back off during the night. After a few bleary minutes, before she heard scraping sounds downstairs. She stumbled up and fell over herself trying to run. She got back up holding her guns, shaking.

Through the dark, she wove down to the window where the noise was coming from. She could hear someone on the other side, pulling at the boards. Then the scrape of a metal tool, prying.

"Get the fuck back!" She brought both guns up and waited. The prying sound stopped.

She stood for a minute, breathing hard. She thought they might have gone, but she couldn't hear anything over her heart pounding. It was an hour before she sat down, but she fell asleep almost immediately when she did.

She slept for hours but it felt like an instant. She awoke to the sound of the kitchen windows being broken. The shattered glass fell into the stainless steel sink and she came to with a high, short scream. She scrambled up and ran toward the kitchen.

A tall man with a blond beard was halfway into the window. He had reached forward to grab the edge of the sink with both hands and pull himself forward, squeezing through. She brought up the gun. He was stuck. He looked up and she could see in his eyes that he knew it.

Both her hands shook. The shot was less than ten feet and she blew it anyway, putting a hole into the bowl of the sink. He jerked and screamed and tried to push backward.

Her nerves were shattered and she could feel herself tearing up. She widened her eyes, forcing them to focus and tried to breathe deep and steady herself.

The blond man came free with a jerk and she saw the two others outside who had hauled him back. Two dark-haired men, also bearded. They goggled at her.

She cleared her throat. "I told you fuckers this place was mine." Her voice broke and she shook all over. They knew her then. It was all over their faces with shock and hunger, and one of the dark-bearded ones made to try his luck with the window.

Dead now for sure. Dead.

She opened fire, both guns blazing, not caring how many

rounds she lost. She didn't hit any of them, but they ran. She stood in the kitchen, waiting. She was making a high, keening sound. She wasn't conscious of it and when she heard it she didn't know where it was coming from.

After a few minutes, she quieted down. She didn't have anything to block the kitchen windows. She closed the door and blocked it with the china hutch. The heavy unit scraped the wood floor as she shoved it in front. When it was there, she went and sat on the couch in front of the fireplace. She waited.

She nodded off, but woke every time her chin came down. She began to feel as if she were hallucinating. Dark shapes darted in her peripheral vision. She woke up swearing, she fell asleep muttering.

Just before sunset, someone slid into the kitchen. In an instant she was awake. She thought she heard two sets of boots hit the floor, but it had been three. The door she had blocked was the only way from the kitchen into the rest of the house.

They pushed against the door, but the hutch was heavy. A long, sustained push might have moved it, but the man on the other side rammed it with his shoulder. The hutch rocked.

She couldn't get her eyes to focus. Terror fought exhaustion and she was ready to kill.

The door thudded against the hutch again. The hutch rocked. The banging grew louder as she assumed the other one had joined him. One became four became five in her frenzied imagination and she checked her clip. She had enough to kill ten, if she could hit them. She tried to steady herself.

I can still get out. I can still get out.

A few seconds of silence.

A splintering crash as the hutch fell facedown into the living room. The base of it was inches from the door. Hands worked their way into the opening and she could hear them straining. The top of the hutch was wedged against the corner of the staircase. She knew it wouldn't move.

She waited. The straining stopped.

One of them spoke into the crack, his mouth pressed into the opening. "We'll be back, sweetheart. All of us. Get ready to come along. There's no other choice."

Bullshit. Let me show you some choices. I've got a clip full of choices.

She heard them scrape through the window to leave her. She went upstairs to the window where she could see their place. She sat on the floor with her chin on the windowsill, watching as they went back into their house.

They waited for morning. She watched.

When the sun rose, she could pick out the shapes of a couple of them standing around their fire pit. They had knives and pipes and other improvised weapons. She knelt on the floor looking at the two guns, deciding. In the end, she chose the new one. She thought it was slightly more accurate at a distance. The shot was a hundred feet, easy. She lined it up slow, breathing deeply. She took the shot. She did not know to account for the drop as gravity acted on the bullet. She had been aiming for his torso, but she could see his kneecap explode when the bullet hit. The morning was still; she could definitely hear the screaming. It scattered the rest of them, and she took three more, wildly, heart pounding too hard to aim. One man dropped outright, and she assumed she had killed him. The other bent over, holding on to himself and screaming.

She got down below the window and waited for return fire, for the sound of someone breaking in downstairs. After a few minutes had passed, she was sure that there were no guns among them. She waited. No sound. When she dared to look again, they were leaving. They left the dead one where he lay.

It wasn't the first time she had killed someone. Threatening close and threatening far away felt different. She sat there with her back pressed to the wall, thinking about that. Knowing she would kill again, deciding what that would change in her. She flashed for one moment on the man dead in her bed, pulling the sheet up over his face.

She didn't look out the window again.

# Chapter Three

*October*

Fucking cold. Started trying on the winter gear I found. Got good wool socks and boots, a couple of sweaters and a ski parka filled with down. Nixed the one that fit me better- it was pink. Pink = girl. Any kindergartner knows that. Everything is baggy except the boots. Was so relieved that they fit I haven't had them off in days. Had to strip off my compression vest and wash it. Standing there, topless and scrubbing this thing felt so strange. Me = not me. My breasts for the first time in ages. Washed them up with my hands and got lost in the sensuousness of it. My tattoo. Like returning to an old lover I left years ago. Can't feel like myself. Finally put it back on when it dried. Felt better dressed. Not me = me. Me not now me then me new. Trimmed my hair again, not shaving it in this cold. Combed it and looked in the mirror. Too clean. Thought about it. Tried to stick some of the hair clippings to my face = doesn't work at all. Used some makeup I found in one of the bathrooms with a sponge to give myself a 5 o'clock shadow. Not gonna fool anyone up close. Distance + hat = maybe?

Bitch I am a man. Females. Talk too much. Quit crying. So emotional. Be a man. Man up. Nut up. Jumpshot gunshot cumshot moneyshot. Posing but not to be sexy. Scare me. Lean a little forward. Invade my space. Quit crying. Give you something to cry about.

Back to the map again today. Have to look seriously at staying here for the winter. Don't want to try and fight my way through snow, but that's a long time from now. Part of the problem = don't know where I'm going. Or what the point is of going anywhere. Going north seems very safe, but only because of the exodus to the south. Colder still and up against the snow = keeps people away. Growing food if I ever get past raiding = all but impossible. Expiration date of body > expiration date of canned tuna. Know when I get there. Maybe just stay here.

*December*

Christmas used to be the best time. Didn't celebrate it, but it cheered almost everyone up. People wore Christmas scrubs and the whole hospital was decorated- almost as much as the stores. Miss Christmas movies and the baked goods. Shit. Baked goods. Fudge and cookies and Christmas cake. Chocolate everything. Rice krispie treats. Nuts and rum balls and brittle and cinnamon rolls in the morning. Donuts. Lonely lonesome only solo alone.

Food holding out just fine, but it sure isn't Christmas. Kill for two hours with a DVD player and a slice of cake. Five minutes of the internet. Boredom is the killing thing. Haven't read all the books here yet, but the day will come. Need more candles. Or a lantern. Something. These tea lights are almost gone. Don't want to raid in the cold, but there's no other way. Need more light.

Three days later and found = shit. 0 lanterns, 0 candles 0

boxes of matches. Went as far as the house where the men were camped out. Lots of porn and food and good knives. Nothing for light, though. Exhausted cold desperately want a fire. A few of the houses = good wood piles.

*December almost January winter solstice? Days so short*

Broke down and started lighting fires. Put out at dawn BUT burn all night = make a difference to my sense of well-being that cannot be overrated. Light from fire = incredible to read by, sound of the crackle = voice. Sleeping in front of it like an old dog. Last lighter is holding out, but have to find a replacement soon.

Place feels almost like home. Got everything set up for me. Putting the garbage out back and pissing outside. Way those guys trashed that house they can't have been meaning to stay.

At least they had each other.

Lone wolf. Lone ranger. Cowboy. Work alone. Great savior. Magic man. Got your magic right here. Don't need anybody. Fine by me. Fine.

*2 January*

Somewhere around the first of the year. New Year's, if anyone is keeping track. Clock calendar bullshit bullshit time. Punch the clock. Time to think about things.

Haven't seen a live dog or cat since the city. Remember seeing cats eating the dead. No dogs. Everyone in the city had a stupid little pug or poodle or designer cross-breed. Saw none at all. Maybe they got the fever, too? Cats 1 Dogs 0.

Seen no deer. This seems like the kind of place that would have deer, but there's no trace of them. Seen birds though. Thousands of birds. If I see geese when it warms up, going to try and shoot some. Fish in the lake. Coming this way = valley = should have seen cows, or smelled them. Didn't, but maybe I just missed them? Raids = 0 rats. Bugs of all kinds no rodents. Maybe plague = most mammals?

Probably twenty five live men since the hospital. Mostly in groups. Three live women: that woman with her daughter in the city, and Jenna. Also me. News said women and children were much more susceptible to the disease, saw that with my own eyes. Didn't put a number on it, but from the hospital = probably ten to one. Saw no children recover. Saw maybe one (?) woman get better before I got sick = Dr. Godey. Government started evacuating the ones that did get better. No live children born to women with the disease + children of uninfected women died within hours of birth=0 kids. Lot of talk about that with the lab crowd.

Have to face the possibility that almost everyone in this country died. Haven't seen military, police, or any aircraft in more than a year. No law = no government anywhere. No power no water. Went to sleep and the world was dying >>> woke up and it was dead and gone. Remember turning on my phone when I came to. Told me there was no network, no hospital Wi-Fi, and its battery was almost dead. Had about a thousand text messages. Scrolled through looking for one from my family, from Jack, but most of them made no sense. Questions = can't answer. Last few texts from Twitter were awful. Suicide tweets >>> broad accusations = conspiracy and germ warfare. Fucking civil defense message system notified = martial law in effect = stay indoors. White House tweeted: everyone should remain calm that help is on the way. My battery dead.

Still have it. Carrying a square chunk of glass and plastic = literally good for 00000. Don't know why. Can't leave it behind.

Remember living in San Francisco, the carnival feeling of FUCKING STOP FUCKING STOP THIS IS WORTHLESS.

Begin again.

Jack .

His name was John, but he was Jack to everybody but his mother. So pretentious. So silly. So much like me. Wish he was here with me. Wish I knew he lived through it. Maybe he's out there somewhere in Texas, treating wounds. Jack = cowboy who lives forever.

Assume that a huge percentage of the population died off, then another percentage died off right after. People who were already too sick or injured to travel, people dying of injuries, infection, untreated cuts and broken bones. Whatever women are left out there having dead babies are probably dying too, from the fever, from lack of care and infection. Killed by the men who hold them, on whatever terms. Jenna made it through though. Maybe not too many are dying, but I don't think there are a lot of women left. Have enough injections for a thousand women. If I ever see any.

So is that the mission now? Angel of birth control, out to stop the crop of dead babies before it starts? Got the morning after pill, but I doubt I'll get to use it on anyone. Wish I could get some RU486. Have the tools to do a D&C if I meet anyone who needs to abort. Can implant an IUD, but passed them over at the university. Too risky without being able to sterilize. Guess this is what can I do. Can make it easier. Can't fix it. Nobody can. Not that different from what I used to do. Every day I remember what Chicken said, = nothing to do now but survive. Doing that now, but it's not the only thing. Can't be. Just gotten to the point where it feels too hard to keep trying. Every woman in labor says she can't do it. Couldn't stop what was happening, but I could make it easier. All the same.

Still a midwife. Thing being born is the world. New ugly baby world.

Mission mission mission impossible so stupid FOR WHAT? Have a purpose. Guess that is the reason to go on. Pathetic. Define me. Always did always will. I AM I AM I AM MY JOB. Punch in punch out sign your name. THUMBPRINT here. Your name your name your name. Spin straw into gold bring babies back from the dead arise from the morgue and walk but never tell never tell never tell anything nothing and I am nobody. Nemo. Nothing. A name is what you have for other people. Have nothing be nothing call my name what is the echo of silence.

Get a hold get a hold get a hold right now. Find the center and hold. Hold.

*****

She gave herself the luxury of a few days of madness. They were dark and deep and held in them the wreck of the entirety of civilization. It crumbles in the individual as it does in the world. There are battles and accidents, there are collapses and plagues. There is silence only when one side wins or everyone has died.

*March around Equinox*

Time to go. Winter spun out forever. Ate everything in the house down to the last box of stale graham crackers. Saved a few cans of soup and baby food for my pack before only the stuff I hate was left. Read every book in that neighborhood. Put on all the weight I can, and my biceps look so developed = wish I could go sleeveless to show everyone how manly I am. Remember the first lady used to have those incredible arms. Past that. Too big, too round for a sleeveless dress. Mannish. Perfect.

Bathed and slept. Rigged up a kind of holster system out of bed sheets. Hope to do better in a place where guns were a bigger deal. Know guns are cleaned out of every store, but maybe some leather holsters are still there. Cut my hair and brushed my beard on again. Early spring = tulips already out by the lake. Got the motorcycle out, oiled it up everywhere the pieces move, filled the gas tank and strapped a gas container to the back. Out in the driveway = can see it.

Place has been great. Holds part of me, now and always. Only had to kill. Didn't have to. Did. Can't think about that. Glad I waited through the winter. Feel strong and ready to travel. Picked out a route that I think won't be too hard.

*May*

Exhausted. Wasted. Sick. Tired. Raining = nonstop. Seen no one for months. Rode the bike until I ran out of gas and couldn't find any anywhere. Walked for miles and miles, had to raid new shoes twice. Haven't been dry since I left the lake house. Haven't eaten in two days = got an upper respiratory infection, won't die. I live you die short lifespan motherfucker I outlive you. I win. In a barn now, as dry as I can get, taking antibiotics and drinking rainwater. Last entry is fucking sickening. Was so sunny side sure it was going to be a picnic out here. Hate everything. Can barely breathe. Going to sleep as long as I can and see if I can get better. Aspirin. Gun in my hand.

Don't know how many days it's been. Fever is gone = woke up starving and dehydrated. Drank all the water I could, but had to go raiding for something to eat. Old farmhouse next to this barn had a can of peeled tomatoes under the stairs of the cellar = delicious. Have a rash and a raging yeast infection = fucking antibiotics but bug is dead. Need a water filter. Water = probably how I got sick.

Map = I'm in Bumblefuck Nowhere, east Oregon. All scrub out here. Billion birds of prey but I don't think they're having a lot of luck besides lizards. Sat out in the sun for an hour, stacking up rocks like they teach boy scouts to do, except don't know the code.

She went thattaway. Tracker and tracked.

Walking for days. Wake up, walk all day. Eat what there is to eat. Lie down in the open and pass out at dusk. Haven't seen a predator or a squirrel. Only the carrion birds and bugs. Not worried about an animal. Can't give a shit about people. Too tired.

Walked for two weeks. Very hungry. Came to a road and followed it, probability be damned. Ran into a gas station, not cleaned out. Sat on the floor and ate about sixty-four handi snacks and drank a gallon of some sugary shit that still had a seal on it. Packed up all the jerky and chips and dried apricots my bag would hold. Gave myself another haircut in the bathroom after pulling a dead man off the toilet. Used his body to prop the door open. For light. Everything stinks, but at least I'm not starving anymore. The road signs say there's a town up ahead. Going for it.

*June*

Town = McDermitt, apparently. Sort of a town. There's an airport. Thought very seriously about trying to fly a plane. Terrible idea = die if I did it. But very tempting. Staying in a saloon. Eating a lot of nuts and pretzels = haven't had good luck. Try houses later this week and see if I can scare up something better.

Turned down a lot of dented cans. Not worth getting sick over. Found dried soup mix, some MREs, and a lot of green beans. It'll do. In one of the houses, found a note painted on the wall, in huge letters somebody did with a brush.

THE MESSAGE OF CARTER
THE YEAR OF THE DYING
AS SCRIBED BY THE UNNAMED MIDWIFE
HAVE GONE TO CALIFORNIA
TAKING RT 101 SOUTH THROUGH SF TO LA
THE BABY IS ALIVE AND WITH ME
FOLLOW US IF YOU CAN
MORE SIGNS ON THE WAY
CARTER

Stared at that for a long time. The baby is alive. With me. Alive. Carter. Wtf Carter? What if he left with a newborn in the short interim between birth and death? What if he didn't know?

What if he actually has a live baby?

Upstairs = wreck of a bloody birth, but no body. Crusty scissors on the floor. Everything soaked with blood gone black. The baby is alive and with me. Ok.

Kitchen was bare except for a can of water chestnuts and another of beets. Packed up both and kept moving. Meet Carter = follow him? Take care of the baby? Figure me out?

Don't know.

*Late June*

Barely got away that time. Met some people out in the road

in McDermitt. I came around the corner and there they were, with hardly a second to react. Hands = free = on my guns= always. Fully dressed and dirty. Five men crouching in the street. Two women on leashes stood, staring. Never forget it as long as I live. As dirty as rescue dogs. Same look in the eye.

*****

"What the fuck?" One man popped up, pulling a gun at his hip. She was just as fast and she had one on him.

A taller man stood up with a machete pulled out smoothly from a strap at his back. "Hey now. Hey now."

"I don't want any trouble," she said loudly. She stared at the leashed women. One was about forty, topless and with a bad implant job. The other was in her twenties, naked, with scabby knees.

The tall guy stepped up to block her view of them. "Neither do we, stranger. Just passing through."

"Me too," she said. "Though, I'll trade if you guys can be cool."

The tall one put his machete back in its sheath and stepped up with his hand extended like he was gonna sell her a car. "I'm Aaron. These guys are Jimmy, Ethan, Manny, and Chuck." They nodded to her. She looked around. White. Black. Asian. The rainbow fucking coalition. All bigger than me. One or two guns, lots of knives. One baseball bat that she could see. She sunk inside. She shouldn't have offered to trade.

Too many. Shouldn't be here and this is too many.

"I'm Carl."

"Carl. What have you got to trade?" Aaron smiled a little and advanced on her.

She put her hand out and waited for Manny to holster his gun. She put hers away slowly. "Food. Medicine. A little booze. Stale cigarettes. Medical attention if any of you guys need it."

"Guns?" That was from Manny.

She shook her head. "Just mine. Guns are hard to find these days. I know where there's a bunch of antibiotics and basic medical supplies, though."

The men exchanged a glance. Aaron spoke first. "What have you got?"

"Penicillin. Ampicillin. Erythromycin. Good stuff. Plus a wound care kit." She waited a beat and watched their faces. "Codeine. Morphine. Fentanyl. Hard stuff." She had more of it than she would ever use before it expired. She saw a few perk up at the mention of the opiates.

"And what do you want?"

"Your girls." She said it flatly, without hesitation. They knew what she wanted. They weren't showing anything else.

Ethan whined at Aaron. "Let him have the old one. Fucking Roxanne. Not Melissa."

Roxanne, the older one, blanched.

Chains. Fuck me sideways. Jenna was one thing. I can't walk away from this. Too many of them. Not a hero.

"I want both. Half an hour each, private. For that, you get a selection of everything."

Aaron smiled a little. "Both is too much. You only need one to get the job done."

She smiled back at him. "Maybe for you. But I haven't seen a girl in a long while. I want both. You'll get them back in one piece."

Ethan again. "Shit we can find our own drugs. We did before, and this skinny fuck did. We don't need this."

"Well, if you're not interested, I'll be going." She shouldered up her bag and made as if to leave.

Aaron took one more step. She was tense all over and trying not to show it. "You alone?"

"Nah." She said it lightly, trying not to sound scared. "The other guys are back at the base, looking out. We just don't have any women."

"You gonna bring the other guys to the party?" He was watching her very closely.

Secure. Totally secure. A little selfish.

"No, fuck them. I don't want a gang bang."

"Why don't you ditch them and come with us, then. We could use another armed man. And we've got two girls. You're a good search man, obviously. You've got medical skills? His eyebrows went up.

"Army medic. Iraq. Four years."

"See? You'd be a good member of our team."

"Where you headed?" She knew the answer.

"South. We heard there was almost no plague death in Central America. Lots more women down there."

Lots of women. Also milk and honey and the streets are paved with gold.

"Yeah, I heard that too. I like my group though. Thanks."

"Suit yourself. So where's this ton of drugs?"

"Back at camp. I'd have to go get it and come back and meet you here. Take me maybe an hour."

"Alright. See you when you get back."

She walked away slowly, not wanting to turn her back on them. They were silent while she left. She walked until she knew they couldn't see her, then ran. She ran around blocks and zigzagged until she almost got lost. She found the saloon again and stood panting, gulping water. She went down into the cellar where she had stowed her pack. She had caught her breath and filled up a bag with a handful of everything. When she came up the ladder, the five men were there, with another guy she hadn't seen.

Damn it.

Aaron looked at her like the devil with a soul to collect. "This is Archie. Our spotter. He was up on a rooftop when you split. Looks like you're all alone after all."

She stared him down. "They're all out raiding," she said.

Breathe slow, talk low. Don't look around, stare right at Aaron. I can still get through this.

"Sure they are. So we're gonna take what we want and then be on our way."

A few beats of silence while she thought about it. Manny and Archie had guns drawn on her, but the two of them stood almost together and not ten feet away. Nobody else had shown a gun. If she let them get close to her, she knew what would happen. They'd take her guns and pat her down. They'd realize what she was and she'd end up on a leash. They wouldn't kill her as long as they figured it out first. She held that thought up to the light and examined it.

Nope.

She dropped the bag to the floor and the sound was an anticlimactic thud. On the other side of the bar, inches away, Aaron pulled his machete. She drew both guns and fired, not really seeing, toward where the two armed men had been. She shot Aaron in the face, close up, as he tried to bring the machete down. She flinched back from the spray of blood, stumbling. She missed Chuck and hit his baseball bat, he dropped what was left of it and ran. She fired again and again, making holes in people, aiming without eyes. She hit one of them in the thigh and he went down, screaming. She winged and grazed and cut them up more than anything. Kept it up until nothing moved. The two who had guns had shot at her and missed, but she never knew it. Her ears rang. She went outside, deaf and still holding her guns up. Chuck was out there, trying to drag both women toward a bicycle, but they were both fighting him. He had his back to the door.

"Drop it."

He looked over his shoulder at her, still holding both leashes. Up closer, she could see they were made of heavy chain with padlocks at the neck. The women looked chafed and sore where the chain rubbed. There was no way they'd get out of them.

"Fuck you."

"I'm holding the gun, asshole. Drop it." She cocked back the hammer on her revolver for good measure. Her hands were shaking. It was a punk line. She didn't know why she said that, why she cocked it. She was going to kill him anyway. She drew it out for no reason.

He turned around and tensed up, to run or pull them in to shield him. She couldn't tell what his plan was. She shot him in the back of the head with the newer gun. His skull caved in and blood came down between his shoulder blades. He collapsed forward with the chains wrapped around his forearms. Melissa, the younger one, fell back on her ass with the pull on her chain. Roxanne stayed upright, staring at the dead man.

They stayed like that for a minute. It was all so absurd that she couldn't comprehend it. She had just shot six men in a saloon. She was a cowboy. She felt nothing. Not remorse, not elation. She was a little sick, a little shocked, but didn't really feel bad. Her ears hurt, her heart did not. She put her guns away and walked forward to yank the chains out of the dead man's hand. Once they were loose, she thought the two of them might run. They didn't. They stood there dumbly.

She turned to Roxanne. "Do you know which one had the keys?"

The leashed woman looked at her as though she had to translate what had been said. "Aaron," she said after a minute. "On his belt."

She walked back into the saloon and found Aaron crumpled up on the floor. She reached into the crumple and felt around for a key ring. She found it, but it took her a minute to work the carabiner free and get them out. She walked back into the sunlight. Melissa was still sitting on the ground, but she had started to cry. The cowboy walked over to her first. Melissa flinched away from her, but she got the key into the lock. The chains slid off the girl and she sat there, naked. She walked over to Roxanne and did the same. She immediately rubbed her neck. They stood there for a minute, deciding.

"If you guys want to come inside, I've got food. And I bet we can find some clothes."

Roxanne looked at her sharply. "So, what? We're yours now?"

The cowboy kicked the chains at her feet and they rattled a little. "No. You're free. You can go wherever you want. I just thought you'd have a better chance of getting somewhere if you ate and put some clothes on."

Melissa still sat on the ground, crying. She walked over to face her.

"Hey. You hungry?"

Melissa shook her head.

"You want a shirt?

She nodded, sniffling.

She sat them down with bottles of water and went to the nearest houses where she had been raiding. She came back with a bottle of olives, a can of peaches, and a pile of women's clothes. The women were exactly where she had left them. The water was gone. She laid everything in front of them and went in for more. The idea of staying in the saloon that night had just about died. She wasn't going to haul the bodies out, and they couldn't sleep with the bodies in there. She grabbed her gear and a case of water. She emerged again to find they had both gotten dressed. Melissa was trying on shoes.

Roxanne was sitting up with her arms crossed.

"I found the best I could. Some of it probably doesn't fit well, but you can hope for better if you raid a store or a mall." She looked at her under the brim of her hat. Roxanne had a stony quality about her face.

"Have you got any cigarettes?"

She rummaged in the outer pockets in her bag. She knew she still had some. "They're gonna be stale as hell."

"I don't care."

She handed Roxanne a book of matches from the saloon and she lit up a menthol and inhaled deeply like a lifelong smoker. She watched the cowboy the whole time.

Melissa finally spoke up. "Where are we?"

"In Oregon, right on the border with Nevada."

"Wow."

"Where did you come from? How did you guys get here?"

Melissa answered first. "I'm from Michigan. I was traveling with my boyfriend, just outside of Detroit. Aaron and some other guys shot him and came and took me. We mostly drove here, but we walked some and rode bikes. I've been on a leash since Vegas."

"That's where they found me." Roxanne was smoking hard and fast now, lighting up a second one. "I was with Nettie. Annette. We worked together. She got away. I was tased and I woke up with the chains on and nothing else."

"Are either one of you pregnant?"

The two freed women exchanged a glance. "No," Roxanne said. "The other girl was. Shawna. She died during the birth and the baby didn't make it. That was last winter."

"Are you having regular periods?"

They both looked at her.

"You're still gonna try and fuck one of us?" Melissa said it with utter disgust.

"Nope. I'm a doctor. I'm trying to help you out."

"She said she had medical experience, Melissa, remember? When she was negotiating." Roxanne looked at the other woman speculatively.

"Oh. You knew?"

Roxanne laughed a dry little laugh that was mostly smoke. "Working in Vegas I have seen every kind of impersonator on the planet, honey. I know a drag king when I see one. You're good. I'm not surprised the guys bought it. But you don't fool me."

Her hat came off. Cowboy no longer. "Well, good. So, periods? Any infections? Injuries? Chance you're pregnant now?"

Roxanne shook her head, inhaling. "Hysterectomy. It saved me a lot of trouble, back in the day. I got a constant UTI from that bunch of dicks that we were with. But I think that's it."

Melissa was thinking, with her brow scrunched up. "I think I had my period this month. Pretty recently. I'm all torn up, though. It burns when I pee. It aches all the time."

After they ate, she dosed them both with antibiotics and painkillers. She explained the dosage to them and gave them each a full run.

"Whatever happens, where ever you go, make sure you take the whole run." They finished off the night with a bottle of cranberry juice from the bar and laid down to sleep in an ugly tract house.

In the morning, she told them both to watch for a pack. Roxanne found hers right away, a high school kid's backpack with a chest strap around the front. It spanned across her ridiculous implants, making them even more prominent.

Melissa searched listlessly, halfheartedly, before giving up.

When the three stopped to rest on an old porch swing and Roxanne had wandered away, she asked Melissa if she wanted a shot.

"Just in case you get… caught again. It'll keep you from getting pregnant and going out like Shawna did."

She stared with big dark eyes. They were empty.

"Have you got anything that will just kill me? Like a painless injection and I'll go to sleep? Like a dog?"

"What?"

"I just want to die. I don't want any more of this. I'll just get caught by some other band of dicks who'll use me as a human blowjob dispenser. Eventually they'll kill me or I'll starve to death. There's no reason to continue with this. Like a lot of morphine, maybe? Something peaceful? I don't want to be shot."

"No… look… there's no reason to die, either. You're ok, in one piece, and you're recovering from what was done to you. That won't happen again."

"It will. Yes it will. There are no women left. Maybe a handful of us. Eventually we'll get used up. I'll get captured again. It's all men out there now."

"Yeah, but they're not all like that."

"Maybe they didn't used to be. What else is there, now?"

They sat in silence for a minute. "Look. I don't want to kill you. I don't want you to kill yourself. But it's your choice. What I'm offering is a load off your mind, just in case… in case you meet a guy you like. Do you want it or not?"

"Sure," she shrugged. She gave Melissa the shot, and a few morning after pills for her pack, when she found one.

Roxanne came back with a pack for Melissa. It was a hideous flowered backpack. Melissa put her pills in it, but wasn't interested in gathering supplies. She ate diffidently and seemed eager to go to sleep.

*****

Slept with my arms wrapped around my medkit. Could have killed herself with any number of things in it, but she didn't. Morning = Melissa just gone. Now we are two. Swing swing bang bang drink poison = win the game.

*****

Roxanne sat up, blinking. "Where the hell did she go?"

She had been up for a while, staring at Melissa's abandoned pack and shoes. "I dunno, but I don't think she's coming back." She didn't want to look for Melissa. She didn't want to find the girl hanging in a garage or slit open in a bathtub. Melissa had made her choice.

"So, do you want to come with me?"

Roxanne dragged on her cigarette. "Who the hell are you, drag king?"

"Call me Ishmael."

"What?"

"Nothing. I'm Alex."

"Where are you going, Alex?"

"North," she said. "East. Away from where everyone else is heading."

"They're all following that radio broadcast."

She looked up, her throat suddenly very tight. "What radio broadcast?"

"The one in Spanish. I didn't understand it, but some of the guys did. You got a radio?"

She didn't, but they found a car with enough battery left to turn one on. Roxanne sat in the passenger seat and tuned it in carefully, finding a very narrow signal.

"...of the Republic of Costa Rica. We have established a survivors colony in our sovereign nation where all those who lived through the plague may come to live in peace. Most of our women did not die, so it is safe to bring your women here. All women, come to the Republic of Costa Rica, where you will be cared for as the mothers of a new civilization."

The message repeated.

Directions followed, complete with coordinates. Alex translated the Spanish Roxanne couldn't make out.

Roxanne laughed her dry laugh. "Sure. Very safe. Bring all your women here. Heh."

"Yeah."

They sat for a little while, listening to the message loop. Roxanne left to pee after a while and Alex carefully dialed up and down the entire radio band, first AM then FM. The Costa Rican signal was the only thing she could find. She turned the car off. She thought about where they were.

*****

No way that broadcast is from anywhere near Costa Rica. What would carry the signal? Somebody wants people to head south, especially women. She came back. Said she would go with me. Didn't tell her what I thought about the radio, but couldn't stop thinking it. Packed up and started off on bikes, to see where we could get.

*July*

Biking and hiking through the sharp rocky hills of Idaho. Some of them are too steep to bike, but we've been dragging them up. It helps speed things along and I know we're making better time than we would on our feet.

*****

They camped out one night in a huge luxury RV they found abandoned at a rest stop along a freeway. It had a glass bubble ceiling above the loft and they both lay on their backs, looking up at the stark and cloudless sky.

"So you're a dyke, right?"

Alex thought for a while before answering. In the old days at nursing school, she had stretched this answer out in long sociological discussions of identity, fluidity, gender normative behavior in a heteronormative society.

Yes. No. Sometimes. Say yes, maybe she'll want to sleep with me.

"I dated mostly women. In school. But my most serious long term relationship was with a man. Whatever you want to call that."

Roxanne smoked and the long curls of it hit the glass and pooled. It smelled awful, but Alex wasn't about to send her away. She cracked the roof hatch.

"I just figured."

"I didn't always dress like a dude. This is a safety measure."

"Yeah but what if you found some people? A guy who could take care of you? He could defend you, hunt for food so you don't have to? What are you gonna do when canned goods run out and you gotta shoot deer to live?"

I just shot six guys. Did she just forget that? Don't fight. Talk easy.

Alex crossed her arms behind her head. "Shoot deer, I guess. Or fish. I haven't seen any deer."

Roxanne turned toward her, up on an elbow. She stubbed out her cigarette and automatically lit another. "We did, when we were in California for a bit. In the hills there were mule deer with huge ears and huge feet. I think you can eat them."

"That's good news. Anyway, why would I sell myself to a bunch of guys who keep me for somewhere to stick it? What kind of deal could I make?"

Roxanne smoked and sighed. "I would have talked myself off that chain. They were just scared we'd run. It wouldn't have lasted."

Alex didn't answer.

"I know what guys are like. I worked the pole when I was younger, then retired into waitressing like everyone does. Guys think they're always in charge, but you can manipulate the shit out of them. We hold all the cards."

"Not anymore."

"What, babies? They don't give a shit. Besides, every man on earth thinks his dick is magic and he'll be the one to turn it all around. You think they don't? You should have seen them fight over Shawna, trying to guess who knocked her up. We still hold the cards."

"If you say so."

"What, you don't believe me?"

"I believe I found you chained up and naked. I don't think you held much then. Didn't you say they tased you and kidnapped you? Didn't I have to treat you for abrasions and infections in your vagina? That's not a lot of cards, is it?"

She was quiet for a long time. "They didn't have a taser."

"So...?"

"Nettie had a taser. She kept it on her since she got raped back in '05. Katrina. She moved to Vegas right after. I met her at a bar and we moved in together. I loved her so much. I didn't have any idea I could love a girl like that."

"I don't understand." Alex turned to look at her, finally. Roxanne's face in the starlight and smoke was like a leather mask.

"Nettie had the taser. We could hear them coming. She gave it to me good right in the neck. To slow them down. So she could get away. I hope she still has it."

Alex stayed awake long after she had fallen asleep. When she finally fell asleep, she dreamt she was an auctioneer, selling every girl she had ever loved to men with long knives. Her dream tasted like ash.

*Let's just say it's the 4th of July*

Fucking Idaho is nothing but hills. Up and down and can't ever see what's ahead. We walk the bikes half the time, but it's still not as bad as walking. Long stretch of nothing so we've been sleeping in the open. Hate hate hate that = hardly sleep at all, but it's what we've got.

Traveling with Roxanne = totally different than being alone. Just having someone to talk to = enormous relief. She's asleep right now. Stars all out and the world is completely full of bugs. Twitches in her sleep when she gets bit, but doesn't wake. Could sleep through anything. Doesn't complain, got a sharp eye. Got to find a place to raid bug spray. Sign says there's a town in 20 miles. Should make it there tomorrow. Hoping for good hunter's bug spray, stacks of jerky, and new cotton underwear. Dreamworld. Really need water and a portable filter = can drink the water we find without worrying.

Of course she asked where I was when it all went down. Guess this is the new 9/11 for those who made it through to remember where we were. Wasn't one day, it wasn't like you were walking down the street and heard that the world was ending. Don't want to do this over and over again. Started as unsettling pictures on the news and then people in some other city were dying. Fucking government closed stadiums and airports, people on the news in yellow suits. Dead people. People in your city, on your block. By the time it was on top of us it was too late to mark the time. Remember where I was, because I was always at the hospital. NO. On call and sleeping when I could, there. NO. Told her some about the deliveries, about the dead and dying women and babies, about getting sick myself and waking up dehydrated, confused, and alone. NO NO NO. Don't want to ask back = polite to ask back. Are we very polite savages now? Gave her the book. Told her to write it down. Fresh page.

## THE BOOK OF ROXANNE

I was living with Nettie in Vegas. She was younger and better looking than me, she was a cocktail waitress at Caesar's. Good tips but she had to wear these killer heels. Her feet always hurt. I worked at Sam's Town. Good crowd, but mostly older. I wore lower heels but balanced it out with this tit job. I made less in tips but more per hour. Neither of us drank, we belonged to the same gym, had a nice little place in Henderson. It was good.

So when the shit hit the fan, nothing really changed. Vegas is like its own planet. Nobody watches the news or wants to think about real life.

Tourists were still pouring in for a week or so, but then I started to see a change. One day it was like there were no Asians at all, and let me tell you, there are more Asians in Vegas than there are in Asia. I came home from work and told Nettie about it and she looked at me with her eyes big and said it was true on the strip, too. We were used to seeing a lot of foreigners but, all of a sudden there weren't any. No Eurotrash, no beautiful black men so dark they were blurple with their strange accents and bright yellow gold jewelry. I couldn't find anybody but drive-in tourists from California and Arizona. I started asking around, listening for New Yorkers or a dumbfuck with a southern accent. It was creepy, like the world was shrinking.

Then they shut down McCarran and everybody freaked. I saw people hitchhiking out of town, offering a thousand dollars for a ride in a minivan, trying to get home or get out. I started seeing sick people on the street. At first I thought I was seeing bad nighttime makeup in the daylight- bright red cheeks and eyes with too much black liner. But these girls had fever. You could feel it baking off of them. Some guys, too. I hit the grocery store in Henderson and it was a mob scene. I bought water and toilet paper and chocolate pudding, don't know what I was thinking. I like pudding. I don't know. I got home and found Nettie sick, laying on the couch, burning up. I took care of her for days. She burned so hot I thought she'd have brain damage. 911 was busy and stayed busy. I locked up the house and made soup and forced her to drink.

The phone lines went out, but I couldn't get anyone to answer anyway. Then the power went off, and the water went with it. After about a week her fever broke. She was skinny and tired, but alive. We had to move to a house with a pool, a block down. It was empty. We stayed there until the water started to grow algae. We loaded up some bottled rich bitch fizzy water and drove to some condos we knew- high end with an indoor pool and all that shit. We stayed there until we got caught.

We were always hiding. We caught on slow that we didn't see any women, and groups of men seemed to be roaming everywhere. The first night in the condos we stayed up on a top floor. We heard screaming outside and we peeked through the window, kneeling on the floor. We saw a gang of maybe ten guys run down this screaming lady- she was maybe thirty. Heavy. She couldn't run for shit and they caught her and took turns at her. At first she screamed and fought and Nettie held her ears and sat down on the floor. Eventually though, she just laid there and took it. They turned her over and pinned her arms and it took them a while to run out of new ideas. When it was over, they had to carry her away. They went toward another high rise and we didn't see them again. Nettie strapped her taser to her leg and told me she wasn't going to get caught and raped. She would fight and she would kill. I nodded, but I didn't know what the fuck we would do if we got caught by that many guys. Probably nothing.

It was maybe ten days later when we were found out. We were on the second floor of an office building, heating up some soup. They must have been watching us, because they came straight toward the building, along the back route we used to sneak in. We had broken some glass and thrown it all over the stairs so we could hear someone coming. They were quiet, but the glass crunching did it. Nettie looked at me with those huge wide eyes. She asked me how many. I couldn't tell her by the sound. She got her taser in her hand and said she was ready. I stood up and faced the door, holding a pipe wrench I had found and thought I could swing. She jammed it into my neck from behind and when I woke up she was gone and Aaron and the guys had started the party without me. I stayed limp, made no noise at all. Manny ate our soup while he waited his turn. When they were done, they helped me up to my feet and said we had to hit the road. Aaron looked at me and said they'd protect me, because there were some terrible men out there these days. He really believed I was better off with them. I could see it.

I didn't talk much. I started learning them the way I used to when I was stripping. Learn their needs, learn what they're sensitive about, learn how to work'em. The key to stripping was never to fuck them, or at least not until they said the right number. I knew that chip was gone, but there were other things they wanted. Reassurance. Something like intimacy. Men don't know how to ask for that, they think they can steal it. When they realize they can't, they know they have no power. I didn't tell anyone I'd had a hysterectomy, I let them argue over whether or not I was too old. The fairly constant gangbang kept me bleeding enough for the illusion to stand.

We were lost for a while. When we found Melissa, I hoped she'd make it. Her boyfriend fought like hell to protect them both but he didn't have a gun. He must have known he would fail. In the end he told the girl to run and he tried to hold them off. He died for her, but he barely got a lick in. They shot him and then ran her down. She cried for weeks. She never stopped, she even cried in her sleep. She was the flavor of the week and I got a little time off. I got convinced I could run away while they were all drunk and I actually tried. That's how we ended up chained. I could have gotten us unchained, eventually. The weather got warmer and we ended up naked almost all the time. Melissa ran blood down her legs seemed like every day. I started getting us small things, baths for instance. It's so much more appealing to fuck a girl who's bathed this week. I started insisting that we get fed the same, hinting about maybe getting pregnant and needing vitamins. And I started picking my favorites and being a little more cooperative with them. I tried to get Melissa to do it too, but she couldn't. She had never turned a trick in her life. I never heard her story, but some things about her I could just tell.

They found Shawna all alone, not even hiding, just walking down the road one day. She was so young. At first I thought maybe sixteen, she was pretty well developed. But she would talk to me when they weren't using her. She turned out to be fourteen. Her whole family had died and she had just been wandering since. She had no skills at all, she had been a good girl with good grades. I told the guys she needed aspirin or something for the UTI she was dealing with. She had been a virgin, she told me crying. They tore her the fuck up. But after a few weeks she was throwing up every morning and getting tired enough to crash in the early afternoon. Poor kid had no idea, she thought she had the fever after all. Chuck and Ethan raided a drug store and came back with a test. She peed on the stick and lo and behold.

The guys put their heads together about everything they had

heard about babies and the fever. More than one of them had heard that all the kids born during the shitstorm had died. They all agreed that none of us had the fever so the kid couldn't get it. So they took care of Shawna. They stopped fucking her, miracle of miracles. They raided everywhere to bring her canned fruit and pickles and asked her what she was craving. I encouraged her to tell them her favorites and mine too, and I used what I know about pregnancy from talking girls through abortions to help out and seem useful.

About the time she started to show, the fights began. At first it was just guessing whose kid it was. They talked every night about who fucked her first, last, longest, hardest. Then they got smart and tried to figure out who had fucked her after she last bled. Jimmy got ragged on pretty bad because he always preferred the asshole to the pussy, so it couldn't be him. Aaron pretty much took for granted that the kid was his and refused to participate. He always acted like he was better than the others, like some kind of natural born leader. Shawna barely knew what it meant or what would happen. She had no kind of guess about the father, and she was afraid of all of them.

Aaron eventually spoke up. He told them the kid was his, Shawna was his, and would remain that way. He would have her and the baby to himself when it was all over, and anyone who had a problem with that could eat a bullet. He said mother and child needed protecting, and that he would protect what was his. That shut down conversation.

He was kind of tender with her. Started calling her "prized possession" or "pride and joy." She didn't see the good in it.

I didn't know what to tell her. If she made some kind of alliance with Aaron, went along with his claim, the other guys might respect that like they respected him. If the kid was black or Asian, that'd make it clear and Aaron might give up. She had no preferences, just terror. She just wanted to eat and sleep with her thin little arms wrapped around her belly.

She was maybe six or seven months gone when shit got real. She started cramping up and bleeding first thing in the morning. I told Aaron to send the guys out for gauze and clean towels and all that stuff. They wanted to move her to a big hospital they had seen back down the road but she was twisted up in agony and we didn't have a good way to carry her. I didn't want to anyway, all the hospitals are full of the dead. We ended up inside a gas station with bottled water and a hunting knife and blue shop towels. Shawna cried and screamed and doubled up in pain. Everybody stared at her except Melissa, who sat down on one of the aisles and ate a couple cans of Pringles.

I got her shorts off and took a look. I don't know fucking anything about birthing no babies, like the slave in that movie said, but neither did the guys. She was bleeding in trickles and gushes and I couldn't see anything. Hours went by with me staring between her legs and telling her to breathe or push or whatever and giving her water. About sundown, she stopped bleeding for a while and just screamed. The guys lit candles and torches and whatever they could find, the place smelled like burning plastic and I wondered about gas or oil or whatever just blowing the station up.

Out of nowhere, Shawna heated up. It was like turning on an electric stove. Her face and joints were hot to the touch, the heat off her thighs was blistering as I sat there waiting. Finally, Shawna bore down and I saw the kid's head. It was startlingly white through all the blood and I told her to push hard. She did, crying and obviously getting weaker. The kid came out all in a rush, like a popped cork. Blood spilled out in a wave behind the baby, soaking me and Aaron, who had come pretty close. He backed up quick to get out of it. The baby was in my hands, tiny and thin. He didn't move or breathe. The cord reached back into her and I left it alone. I patted him, I smacked him, I tried to clear his mouth. He was blotchy and blue and never drew a breath. I told Aaron to hold him. I handed the kid off and Aaron wrapped him in shop towels and tried to stir him. The guys offered a few lame suggestions, but they petered out. None of us knew what to do.

Shawna lay limp on the floor, still bleeding out and turning white. I checked her pulse the way they do it in the movies. I felt something tiny tick under my fingers, like a bug under a picnic blanket. She was cooling off. I tried to hold her up and slapped her face a little. No reaction. I pulled at the cord and the placenta gushed out with another bucket load of blood behind it. How this skinny kid could have so much blood to give up, I don't know. With it out, I could see that the kid had ripped her wide open. I couldn't tell what was what down there, she was just shreds. I packed shop towels between her legs and laid them together to the side. There was nothing I could do.

I told Aaron she was going to die from blood loss. He looked at me, holding the baby that had never breathed. They all stood around, staring. Nobody knew what to do or say. After a while, Aaron laid the baby down in Shawna's arms and we left them there together. Melissa got hauled up by her elbow, still holding two cans of those awful chips. The chains went back on. Nobody talked about Shawna or the baby. Two days later I got to wash the blood off me. Things were pretty much the same after that until we ran into you."

Back to me

Wish I hadn't read her story. Felt that sick rush I had always felt after a bad birth. Adrenaline and disappointment = sick. Pity. Held back a thousand medical questions about the birth. She probably wouldn't know the answer and it's not like it mattered. Couldn't stop thinking about the hospital where I saw it all fall apart. Every baby dead. Almost every mother dead. Creeping fever that came from nowhere, we never even really figured out how it spread. No tourists from Asia or Europe. No planes overhead. Maybe not just this country, maybe everywhere. Maybe the world.

Almost dawn now. Going to sleep for a while. Morning I'm going to suggest we skip Pocatello, there's likely people there. We should swing south and raid in the small towns, maybe head for Colorado. Lots of nice cabins that way to hide out in. Maybe make camp for a while.

*Mid July*

Hot as shit and sticky every day. Found a sporting goods store a few days back that had good bug spray. It smells like death and probably causes cancer but I don't give a fuck. Mosquitos beware. Also found a couple of water filters and filtering canteens, small expensive ones. Incredible = not carrying gallons of bottled water. Just drop and filter in any lake or stream or puddle we find. Huge load off my mind. Filters won't last forever, but at least now we know they work and how to find them.

* * * * *

Roxanne and Alex had some good nights. They played checkers in an old diner while they ate a whole can of strawberry pie topping, sugary glaze and all. They talked about where they would go, what they would look for in a place to make a stand. Alex sang a little and Roxanne said she missed the piped-in music of the casino. Roxanne read trashy romance novels that she found along the way, sometimes reading passages aloud.

"His throbbing member aroused her, though she had never known the touch of a man before!"

They giggled like girls and rode along an old highway, not another living thing in sight. Roxanne told terrible jokes she had learned from customers while she worked. Alex told her the standard nursing jokes and apocryphal stories of men with their dicks stuck in vacuum cleaners, in coke bottles, in improvised cock rings. The legendary drill to remove the champagne bottle from an unwise asshole.

They raided a little cul-de-sac of houses. Corpses were drying out all over. The smell wasn't as bad as when they were wet, especially when they opened the windows. Alex found a full bottle of Oxycontin and kept it for trade. Roxanne looked for a gun of her own. She searched the hidden places in those houses, under beds and high in closets.

One house had a wall safe in an office and she was convinced there was a handgun in it. They slept in the den, on big soft couches laid out on a sunken floor. In the morning, Roxanne was in the office right at sunrise, searching. The office had a huge aquarium on one wall. The water had all evaporated and the room smelled like the rotting fish. Alex opened the window that faced the backyard, thinking it was safer than the one that faced the street. The air and light came streaming in and she helped Roxanne look.

The office was like a checklist of prestigious artifacts. Green glass banker s lamp with a brass body. Oak desk like an aircraft carrier. Large blotter and Mont Blanc pen lined up next to Franklin Covey day planner. The dead man in the bed upstairs had likely thought himself pretty important. A tiny blue book in one drawer held account numbers, passwords, credit cards numbers, and five crisp hundred dollar bills folded in half. Roxanne slipped the money into her bra without looking at it. Alex stared at her for a moment before they both burst out laughing. When the moment passed, Roxanne dug it back out and set it gently down on to the desk.

"Maybe he didn't want to write it down," Alex offered.

"He would. Thinks he's fucking James Bond." Roxanne went back to staring at the book, scowling. "He was the kind of guy who wrote down all his passwords, because he's worried that he'd forget someday."

Alex shrugged and let her obsess. An hour later Roxanne was still working. Alex checked the kitchen and found the pantry untouched. They feasted on tuna and tomatoes and beans and Alex ate a whole can of peaches while Roxanne turned the pages again and again.

Roxanne laughed abruptly. "Last page. In case of emergency, call 354-610. That's only six numbers."

She walked to the wall safe and dialed it in, 35-46-10. The door swung open and pulled it wide, excited and pleased with herself for figuring it out.

Stacked up inside the case was an obscene amount of cash. Banded perfectly pristine stacks of hundreds, from the bottom to the top. Roxanne clawed it out on to the floor, hoping for something else behind it. No luck. Bands of bills hit the floor and spread out, sliding against one another, whispering paper defeat. Nonplussed, Alex sat down again.

Roxanne stood there, looking at it.

"No way a guy has this much money and no gun. There's a gun here."

"Roxanne, maybe he was really anti-gun. Maybe he had hired goons. You don't know that there's a gun here."

"There is. There is."

By the third day, Alex wanted to leave. Roxanne would not be moved. Alex sat, frustrated. She read the magazines in the bathroom. She did inverted pushups on the stairs.

Roxanne did not give up until she found it. She had been right all along, and she found it. After several days, she was muttering, all day long.

"Little dicks. All little dicks have guns. He's paranoid about the money. He was into something dirty. He thinks he can't trust anyone so he needs serious firepower. Helps him sleep at night."

Alex had stopped trying to talk to her. Roxanne was trying to get into a dead man's head and it was starting to scare her. Roxanne didn't eat for almost a day, pacing the bedroom with the corpse. She dragged the mattress off to one side, with his dried out body stuck to it. The gun was not underneath. The gun was not hidden in a flour canister or in the basement. She tore everything out of the linen closet, checked the freezer and ended up letting out an unbelievable enclosed stink of rotting meat. It was not on top of the high kitchen cabinets, where there was an inch of dust and dead bugs. The gun was not under the bathroom sink or the kitchen sink and there was not a single loose brick in the fireplace. They always went back into the office, where money carpeted the floor. She flopped down into the big leather chair and Alex sat on the desk.

"It's ok," Alex told her. "You'll find one."

"There's one here," she insisted again. "I can feel it. I know this guy. He has a big motherfucking gun in his house. Maybe his wife doesn't know, but I know. He likes to hold it sometimes and repeat snappy one-liners from action movies. It's here. He's just got it hidden somewhere clever."

The next night they slept on the same big couches. Alex fell asleep right away. She woke when she could hear Roxanne pacing and muttering.

"Roxanne. Come on, lay down and get some sleep. You can't search for shit if you're tired."

"I'm cold." She said it shortly, and Alex knew she was using it as an excuse to stay up and obsess.

She sat up and kicked the lid off the ottoman in front of her. She had seen a hundred like it at friends' houses, especially the ones who had kids. Sometimes they were full of toys or junk hidden just before company arrived, but usually they were full of blankets. She pulled out a puffy comforter in melon green and held it out to her. Roxanne looked over at her, not understanding.

"Blankets. You're cold, right?" Alex reached back into the ottoman to get another for herself, and as she picked it up something rattled underneath.

Roxanne perked up at the noise and crossed the room toward the ottoman. Where the blankets had been there was a folded white sheet, and she pulled it out as a bunched blur and threw it on the floor.

"I KNEW IT." She screamed out the words and all her frustration from this week was in them. "I fucking knew, I FUCKING KNEW he had a gun." Reaching in again, she pulled out a box of bullets. And then another. And another.

She opened a box and held up a fat slug. "There is a gun here. This proves it."

"Alright. Yes. You were right. There's a gun here. Now can you please fucking relax so that I can sleep?"

Roxanne smiled at Alex and sat down on the couch beside her. "Sorry," she said. She pulled up the melon-colored blanket and laid Alex down, tenderly. Without any discussion, Roxanne laid down with her. The couch was long and deep and there had always been enough room, they just hadn't done it before. Roxanne's legs tucked neatly behind hers and she laid her head on the opposite armrest. With their bodies close together under one blanket, they were warm immediately and Alex drifted off fast. Alex slept deeply, sweetly, in the simple contact with Roxanne's body.

She dreamt she was with Jack and when she woke up she had a ghost of grief beside her. She put the ghost away and looked over at Roxanne.

We should do this every night.

They packed up what they wanted to take. Alex searched the kitchen again and found a jar of instant coffee. Bliss. Roxanne was so focused on finding the gun and didn't give a shit about the coffee. She turned down the expensive lotion and the jar of marshmallow fluff.

Out of things to do, Alex paced the living room. She stopped to check the side windows over and over again, to see if anyone was in the neighborhood. She saw nobody out on the street. She turned back to tell Roxanne and saw she was walking across the room to the mantel. It held an old wedding picture, a college grad photo and some small grandchildren in tasteful frames. In the middle there was an ugly little mantel clock, the kind that's round in the middle with little wings off the sides.

She turned back to Alex suddenly. "What time is it on the clock in the study?"

"I dunno, like three thirty or something."

"Right, and three thirty in the bedroom, too." She looked back at the mantel clock. The hands on it pointed to dead midnight. She put both her hands on it, searching it all over. She pulled the plug out of the wall. On the back of it, she found the catch and the face of it dropped open like a drawbridge.

Inside was a .357 Magnum . A ridiculously large gun, a cannon. An expensive prop for an insecure man. Roxanne picked it up and held it.

"It's so heavy."

Alex watched her raise it in a two-handed grip toward the far wall, testing the weight of it. She looked at it through one eye, using the sight at the end of the barrel.

It's loaded. Any asshole who owned Dirty Harry's gun and kept it in a hokey little hideaway like that clock would be stupid enough to keep it loaded and ready to kill imaginary intruders.

It was on the tip of Alex's tongue to tell her.

Before she could, it went off. Roxanne had squeezed the trigger just enough. The gun bucked hard and just missed her face, landing on her shoulder but she still held it in both hands. The sound of it was like an explosion. Alex crouched instinctively with her hands over her ears. The hole it put in the wall of the room was wide and jagged. Alex could see the pitted drywall and the stud underneath. She turned to Roxanne, furious.

She took one look at Roxanne's face and the anger drained out of her. She looked terrified. Stricken. She had had no idea what would happen, or that the gun had been loaded at all.

"Have you ever shot a gun before?" Alex could hardly hear herself over the ringing in her ears.

She shook her head. Alex sighed and walked over to her. She looked so shaken Alex couldn't help but hug her. Roxanne held on the gun but wrapped her arms around Alex anyway. Alex could feel her struggling to get control of her breath.

"Sorry."

Alex pulled back to look at her. "It could have been worse."

She nodded, and kept the gun carefully pointed at the floor.

"We'll have to practice."

"How did you learn it?"

Alex thought about all the time she had spent with her dad and the momentary lapse into nostalgia triggered an empty howling in her heart. His face was sharp in her mind and she ached with grief. He was holding her, he was holding his guns. Using the range at the station to practice with the little .9mm he let her use when she was small. She remembered the .22 she got for her sixteenth birthday and how much her mother had hated it. She called her husband a tea partier, a gun nut, a throwback. Nothing stuck. He didn't care. He voted Democrat with the union, every time. He voted for gun control and the assault weapons ban and any move toward licensing or registration that came up. Alex had heard him say more times than she could remember that people who didn't know how and when to use a gun had no business owning one.

He was a good man. Not the last one.

She looked back at Roxanne. Her face was so naked and lost that Roxanne was shocked for a moment, waiting for her to focus and toughen up.

"I learned from my dad. I'll show you."

In their last two days at the house, they worked on the gun. How to hold it, how to stand. How to use the safety. How to load it, clean it, carry it. Alex wished Dirty Harry had a pancake holster for this thing. Alex hated the gun in her waistband. It was too heavy, too bulky, and there was no hiding it. Roxanne didn't care.

Both of them armed, they got back on the road. Alex was glad for her. Roxanne needed practice firing it, but so far she was still too scared of it. She walked taller, seemed happier just having it made her feel better.

*August First*

She's gone.

# Chapter Four

*Mid August*

Getting used to being alone again. First thought =alone solo just lonely and scared, but now I think I hate her. Hate that she wouldn't stay with me. Hate that I wake up in the middle of the night looking for her. Not like she was with me forever. Not like I got used to her. Shouldn't hurt me forever. Hate hurt hate. Fuck this and fuck you.

September

Hoping to make it into Colorado, but Utah is slowing me down. Everything = dry. Hasn't rained in a long time here and I spend all my time raiding water. Coming near to Salt Lake and there is crazy shit painted on every billboard, every sign, every house I pass. The roads are haunted.

PERKINS-GATES FAMILY: HEAD FOR THE CAMPGROUNDS

STAY OUT OF PROVO- EDWARD TIMSON

THE TIME HAS COME

THE WHITE HORSE MUST GO TO THE ROCKY MOUNTAINS

HOWARD AND EMILY GRAY HAVE CLEAN WELL WATER, HEAD EAST ON 80

TOWARD JORDAN MEADOWS

Run of houses, marked with an X. Don't need a key to translate. X = everyone inside = dead.

*September 18 maybe just guessing at this point*

Small town called Eden - what else? Everything in Utah has a weird bible vibe. Every building I scouted was empty. Every house and office and store. No live people, no dead people = rapture really happened. Raided the general store and walked straight through the center of town with a shopping cart. Population of this town < 500 before, no sign of anyone. For months. Dust is thick on everything.

Found a house with a pantry that was stocked with the idea of famine or siege. Enough here to keep a large family for years. Sealed drums of water, flour, sugar, Bisquick, and rice. Kits for 12 kinds of freeze-dried potatoes. Cans and cans of soup, fruit, veg, chocolate sauce. Lots of empty spaces on the shelves, but I could have skipped the store altogether. Whole place locks up tight, well out back, and three perfectly oiled rifles in a glass case. Five slots in the case stand empty. Drawer underneath is full of shells = home of a survivalist. Must have died in a hospital = there's no sign of them here. Going to stay a while. Can't carry three rifles but I can hold this place down. Wish Roxanne was here.

Still hurts. Starting to understand why she left me.

What happened with Roxanne was we were riding through the last bit of Idaho on a great day. Wasn't too hot but the day was long and golden and we were laughing at some stupid story she had told. Looked over at her while she laughed, seeing the way she threw her head back and started feeling for her. Not falling in love or anything but just that first tenderness of liking, of really digging somebody's details = way more than I used to feel about a coworker who showed up with donuts or somebody who waved me in when traffic was awful. Appreciation of niceness in another person. Sweet.

* * * * *

They came over a hill and there he was.

He sat astride a huge Harley, but it was perfectly in proportion with him. He was massive, with wide bulges of muscle in a black t-shirt under a black leather vest. His thinning dark hair was pulled back in a ponytail. The legs in his jeans were wide and rock-hard, and his motorcycle boots were probably a size 13. He looked up at us rolling helplessly downhill toward him, his face breaking into a huge open smile. No sunglasses, Alex could see his brown eyes sparkle like the eyes of a puppy. He was so happy to see them.

Alex skidded and wobbled, trying to stop. Roxanne yelped a little and fell in the road, dumping her pack behind her. The huge guy got off his bike and loped toward her. Alex dropped her pack and drew one gun on him.

"Don't move."

He didn't hear her or he didn't care.

He got to Roxanne and she was already standing up, getting her bearings. He saw the gun at her waist and drew up short. He looked back at Alex and caught on.

"Hey," he said, hands immediately up in the air. "Hey, it's cool. I'm cool. We're cool."

"Who are you with?" Alex was trying to look everywhere at once while keeping her eyes on him, look for signs of a group, to see if someone was coming to join him.

"Nobody! It's just me. I've been alone for a long time, that's why I was so glad to see you."

"You got a gun?"

"I got a toy gun in my saddlebags that I painted black, in case I need to scare somebody. Not a real one."

Alex popped her chin at Roxanne to tell her to look. She pulled it right out. "Plastic." She dropped it back in with some scorn. She rifled through the rest of his belongings. "Nothing."

"Ok." Alex lowered her gun "We are going to walk away, slowly. I'm going to be watching you. If you try any stupid shit, I'll kill you. I'm not gonna take your motorcycle or shoot you just for fun, and you're not gonna do anything dumb. Ok?"

"Wait! Shit, no please wait. I haven't seen a single human being in months. Please just let's talk for a little while. Please? Look, my name's Duke. What's your name?"

Alex didn't answer, but Roxanne did. "I'm Roxanne."

He turned toward her, beaming. "Like the song! You don't have to put-"

"I hate that fucking song," she cut him off. She lit a cigarette.

"Come on, let's take a break here and talk to him a little. What's he gonna do?"

Alex fumed at her. That fucking gun. She thought she was invincible with it.

"Fine." Alex dug in her bag and got out some oatmeal, her least favorite thing. She started a small fire on the roadside to heat it up and Duke hauled a can of sausages out of his bag. He roasted them over the small flames. When they were crackled, he offered them to the women. Roxanne took one but Alex turned him down to eat her shitty oatmeal. Roxanne gobbled up the smoked sausage and smiled at him.

I hate them both.

"So, where you from?" She asked him with her cocktail waitress charm turned on.

What does she expect for a tip?

He jumped right in. "Montana. I was on a run with a bunch of guys who got sick. When I headed back into Detroit, the city was burning down, so I just turned back out and kept going. I guess it got pretty bad and damned near everybody died. I've just been riding and looking for people. But there was hardly anyone in Montana before this plague. I know I saw some people outside Detroit, but they hid from me. I guess nobody trusts anybody these days. I get that. But I'm going crazy with nobody to talk to."

Roxanne smiled at him and Alex knew right then. This was the end. She saw it coming.

"Where are you two headed?"

"North," Alex said.

"Who knows?" Roxanne said at the exact same time.

"Well, I wanted to head out to California, maybe the cities where there used to be millions of people. The winter'll be easy there and I'll find somebody. Why don't you come with me?"

"Nope," Alex said. "We travel alone."

"Well now wait a minute," Roxanne said. "It might be nice to have a man around, just in case."

Alex stared at her. She hadn't changed her look at all. She was clearly still trying to pass as male. Roxanne had just done it to make her feel exposed.

Duke looked Alex up and down quickly but didn't say anything. He wasn't stupid.

"We've run into some trouble on the road," she said.

She's looking at him like a princess in a fucking tower.

"Rapists and murderers. I was thinking we could use some muscle, just in case we run into that kind of trouble again."

"I would be happy to defend you ladies," Duke said with a shine in his eyes. Every man on earth thinks his dick is magic. Alex could hear Roxanne saying it in her head the day they had met.

"I don't need defense." Alex stood up and kicked the empty can of oatmeal away. "I got it. Roxanne, let's go. He's had some conversation, we're done here."

Duke looked at her, his need plain on his face.

Now he's the princess. Climb on up, Roxanne.

Roxanne looked back and Alex could see her sizing him up like a butcher looks at a cow.

She knows she has an opportunity to trade up. She's not stupid. Or new at this.

"Let's camp here for tonight."

"It's not even sundown yet."

She made a little-girl face. "Yeah but I'm tired. And I want to talk with Duke some more." She turned her eyes back to him and he smiled like an idiot.

Alex unrolled her sleeping bag and made camp. She did her best to ignore them. She wrote in her journal and refused conversation. She looked up at one point and saw him teaching her how to hold the gun. It was exactly the way Alex had shown her, but she was pretending not to know anything at all.

*Next day*

Alright, so he can hunt. He couldn't have done it at all if she didn't hand him he gun like she had no sense at all. He blew a goose out of the sky, first shot. Flying low anyway. Geese scattered, honking. Flopped down in the dirt, dead with almost nothing left above the neck. He says they're all flying south and we should see a lot of them soon. Says you have to aim for the head, because hitting the body will destroy what you can eat on it.

Plucking the fucking thing now. Roxanne is so pleased she can't sit still. She set up a rotisserie-rig made out of tent poles and a long stick. They're going to roast it and eat it. I don't want any.

Fresh goose is delicious. Going to shoot one the first chance I get.

* * * * *

Duke relaxed a great deal after dinner. He took one long drink from a bottle he drew from his saddlebag and offered it around. Both women refused.

Roxanne was the one to get him talking, but they both wanted to know.

"So, what did you hear about the plague?"

He leaned back and looked up at the sky, watching the smoke from their fire drift upward. "Not much, really. One of the guys on the run was worried on the first day, saying his kid sister was in the hospital. I had heard rumors about some kind of flu infecting nurseries and daycares and whatnot. He said she had gotten real sick at the school where she worked and spent a day at home before her roommate took her in to the ER. So this guy was checking his text messages constantly. The guys made fun of him for always being on his phone, but he never did it while riding, so I didn't mind. Anyway, one day he said he can't get his newsfeed to work. He had been telling us the news was weird and that there were maybe riots in L.A. or somewhere. But when he went back on when we stopped for the night, he couldn't get anything."

He shifted his position and realized they were both staring at him intently. "What's the matter?"

"We just haven't heard much of the news. Either one of us. We were both kinda out of the loop, you know?" Roxanne smiled at him in that helpless way.

"Alright. I guess that makes sense. I don't know everything either, but maybe I heard different than you two. So, that same night one of the old guys on the run finally turns his phone back on. He was the kind of guy who had it for emergencies, but you could never get him to pick it up. He logs onto his Facebook and right away we can tell he's upset. He dials up his voicemail and tells us his wife's real sick and they've been looking for him. We tried to talk him out of riding home, but he lived in Indiana and he said he knew the way so well he could do it in his sleep. He took off right then.

"After that, every one of those guys and their old ladies checked in. They turned their phones on, made calls, listened to their voicemail. One after the other, they had to leave. Sick wife. Sick kid. Sick girlfriend. Dead girlfriend. After that night, there were only about ten of us left."

"Didn't you have anybody to worry about?"

Duke looked a little embarrassed. "My mom. I was never married. But I turned my phone on and… well… my mom wouldn't have said shit if she had a mouthful. I thought about it, but I waited until morning. I didn't want to believe the run was over, I look forward to it every year. But some shit was clearly going down. In the morning, even more guys were gone. The rest of us decided to call it and take off. The whole way to Detroit, I thought about my mom. She lived in a shitty little house in one of those neighborhoods they show on TV when they want to talk about what a shithole Detroit is. But I couldn't even get close. I got close enough to see the fire and smell it. It smelled like gas and burning tires and hot paint. I knew there was nothing worth going in for. I still didn't understand, I was pretty freaked out. I saw a group of guys on the road that day. They were just walking. I yelled at them and waved, trying to get them to talk to me. They turned and ran like they saw the devil. Man, Detroit could burn down and that wouldn't surprise me, but I never saw that kind of fear from a bunch of men! Sometimes I know I scare women or little kids… I'm just big. But that freaked me more than anything. What did they think I was gonna do?

"So I got back on the road and got off in the first town I saw. I was having a hell of a time getting gas. I started refilling when my tank was only half empty, and I picked up that jerry can you see there. I had to siphon gas out of cars and tankers… and there just wasn't anybody, anywhere. Cars stood open in some places, and every gas station was deserted. I started seeing dead people, here and there. That creeped me out so bad. I couldn't stand it. If there was dead people, I'd leave and find gas or food elsewhere. I started to feel like a ghost.

"So I was stealing gas at this Shell, station, using a siphon to suck it out of the underground tank after I pried open the cover. I finished filling the bike and the canister and I went inside the station. Nobody was dead in there, so I washed my mouth out with half a warm coke and drank the rest.

"I walked over to the newsstand and there was hardly anything there. The Times was sold out, but the local paper had no stories, just a directory of where to go. Red Cross sites, schools turned into disaster shelters. And two places where you could take bodies. There was a box at the bottom talking about gloves and masks and communicability."

He sounded this word slowly, one syllable at a time. He had struggled with it in the Shell station, knowing it was a word he had heard but had never had to read it to himself before. He knew its meaning from context, as we know all words, but he could not have defined it if asked.

"The one big paper they had left was the Washington Post. It had a picture of the president on the front page and the story said he was hiding in an underground bunker somewhere. They had pictures they said could prove it. The bottom half had an article about death toll in the major cities. The Post was always full of shit, but they were saying ninety eight percent fatality in men."

Alex perked up at that, unable to maintain her stony silence. "Ninety-eight? You're sure that's what it said?"

"They used the number instead of the words, and it was on this huge pie graph. I'm sure."

No way it was ninety-eight percent of men. That would mean it was more than ninety-nine percent of women. That's insane.

"But women were dying way more than men in San Francisco."

Duke was nodding solemnly. "The Post said that doctors were saying the plague was harder on women and girls than men and boys, but they didn't put a number on that."

Roxanne looked stunned. "That's not… there's no way. There would be almost no one left."

"You see anyone around here?" Duke wouldn't look at her. None of them could look at each other.

Alex thought about the number of people she had seen, dead and alive. She thought about the dead bodies piling up at the hospital. She added up impossible numbers and she could not make herself believe it.

Duke was looking down at the dirt. "I don't know what the name of that town was, but when I was headed back out to the freeway, I went by the city dump. I could see huge piles of corpses. Burned. Black pyramids in the middle of all that garbage. I couldn't look at that long. I stayed on the road until I ran out of gas, and then I used the tank to refill. I couldn't go back into a city until I was bone-dry and had to walk the bike down an off-ramp. I felt like the last man on earth."

They slept fitfully that night. He was not the last man on earth. They were not the last women. But the number was small and getting smaller every day.

One more god damned day

Told Roxanne it's been three days and I'm done. They slept cuddled together last night, after Duke told his story. She waited a while, and then just picked up and laid down beside him. Spooning. Not fucking, but on their way. Remembered the way we slept in that den where we found her gun. Empty = lonely = haven't eaten all day and starving but you don't know it until someone brings it up.

Well fine. That's fine.

*****

Roxanne gave her companion a long look.

"You should come with us. We've come together this far."

Duke spoke up from a few feet away, packing his saddlebags. "You ladies ready? We should cover some miles today, make up for lost time."

Roxanne looked over her shoulder. "One second."

He kept talking, mostly to himself. "Can't cover much ground on bicycles. Gonna have to find motorcycles or one of those little scooters. The Euro jobs, like a Vesta or what the fuck ever. They're easy to handle."

Roxanne was already packed and ready to go. She made it seem like she was arguing, but she knew how this would end. "Come on, you can't take off by yourself. Don't end it like this."

I can't I just can't and I don't know why. But you shouldn't go either.

Their eyes met. "Don't go south. I don't know what that broadcast is about, but I don't think it's good news. You might want to let him carry the gun. He's a good shot. You haven't learned to handle it yet. Convince him you two should hole up somewhere. Don't risk another group of guys. It won't end well."

"You're really not coming."

"I can't."

Roxanne turned back to Duke. "Can I ride behind you?"

He lit up. "Yeah! Yeah, I've ridden with a passenger that way lots of times. No sweat. And we can find you a helmet and ride slow so your friend can follow."

"Nope, you two go ahead." Alex tried to sound sunny, just a change of plans. Not abandoned.

She picked up the bike and got ready to leave. Roxanne walked over to her and she waited, head down, for what she would hear.

"Come on, don't be like that. We're both safer traveling with a man. You know that. He's harmless, look at him."

Don't do this. Don't make me tell you how it will end. Stay with me.

"He is harmless. Like Melissa's boyfriend was. You're not safer just because he's bigger with a dick. He can die like anyone else."

"Yeah but the two of us are just sitting ducks."

"With guns."

She dropped a hand to the butt of her comically large firearm. Alex looked there and not at her face.

"You feel better with him because he's a guy and you can probably get him to die for you. Fine. Best of luck to you both. Mazel tov. But I'm taking off."

They both knew Duke could hear them. They didn't care.

"You trusted me to watch you while you slept, to go with you. Why not him?"

"I don't know. It's a feeling. This doesn't feel like a good idea."

Roxanne shook her head, turning away. "You just can't stand the idea that you might not always be in charge. Good luck, sweetheart. Be careful out there."

For a moment, it looked like Roxanne might reach out and touch her, hug her, make one last gesture. Instead she just walked away, back toward Duke. "Let's go," she said to him.

Duke smiled and raised a hand. Alex gave them a half-wave and got on her bike, pedaling away against the rise of the hill, slowly and laboriously. As she sweated up the hill she hoped they weren't watching. When she reached the top she heard the ripping sound of the Harley starting up. She looked back and saw them one last time. Roxanne sat behind him with her arms wrapped around his thick torso and her pack on her back. His ponytail whipped in the wind and picked up like a flag as they accelerated. They didn't look back and after a minute even the sound of the motorcycle was lost to her.

*October*

Duke = probably a nice guy. Duke = probably will die for her. She'll probably end up somewhere terrible. Never know.

Starting to snow.

Need to go out a few more times for supplies and then I'm going to hole up for the winter. Already way too cold. Going to build a fire and keep it going. Haven't seen anyone since Roxanne left. Not a soul. Franklin stove in the kitchen that I can cook on and a fireplace in the main room. Going to lock up, string cans or whatever = alarm system, stay armed. Fuck it. Going to be warm.

Need to gather all the cut wood I can find at neighboring houses = walking and a lot of hauling, might take a couple days. Not worried about water = boil snow every day. Can't get cleaner than that. Want to go to town once more and see about some serious weather gear. Need some gloves and I'd love to find snowshoes or just better boots than I've got. Feet = always cold.

Miss the weather guy. Hate to take off not knowing how bad it's gonna be. Also need a map of town. Don't know if I could find my way back and none of the maps I had went into Utah. Wasn't planning to go into Utah. Where was I going? Don't know that = could end up anywhere. Kind of stupid to keep anyplace off my list at this point. What's to complain about? Politics. Blue laws. Price of real estate. No good schools here. Ha ha. Fuck.

Have to go soon. Even without a weather guy common sense = snow gets worse as the winter goes on. First thing = find house keys.

# Chapter Five

Two days later she walked out into a light flurry of snow, headed back to town the way she had come. The day before, she had busily piled dry firewood into a wheelbarrow she found in a shed and trucked it to her assumed home, making piles inside and on the porch. The second day she set out for town. The constant motion of the snow made her nervous, and her eyes tracked movement everywhere, her heart racing and slowing. She forced herself to get calm but she had to put her hand on her gun to do it. She thought to herself of the way babies soothe just being near the breast, just having the pacifier to comfort them. A gun certainly pacifies.

The street turned on to the main drag of the little town. Flat storefronts faced the road like the set in a Western. She kept close to one side, glancing up to the windows every few steps. Nothing stirred. The unnatural calm and ringing silence of snow pleased her somewhat. She would hear something moving near her, she was sure of that.

She saw the general store, and a small specialty shop that seemed to sell honey and bee-themed tchotchkes of the kind that would delight tourists. She found the post office, useless and littered with papers. She passed a drug store without a thought. She was over-prepared for medical emergency. She did not run into any store she thought would sell cold-weather gear. She doubled back to the post office to see if there was a map of town.

There was a map, but it couldn't be removed from the wall. For a moment habit took over and she fished out the cellphone that hadn't made a sound in over a year and went to take a picture of the map. She laughed softly when she caught herself. She put the phone back gently in her pocket.

Studying the map on the wall, she made a note of the street where her little house stood at the end, separated from the main road and other houses by a considerable gap. She nodded at that gap. She loved it and believed in it. Space. Looking back up, she saw where she was and that there was a feed store a little less than a mile away. They might have farm equipment and items she could use. One more long look at the map and she was out the door.

The feed store had recently had a fire. On one side of the building, hay was scattered around the blackened brick façade. It had obviously been put out before it had spread, but not cleaned up. She stood in the road, staring at that a long time. She knew hay was pretty flammable. She thought back to the fires and evidence of fires she had seen. In the cities, mishaps had turned to disaster and there was no fire department to put things out. All of Oakland had burned down, it seemed. Duke had said the same thing about Detroit.

But this place hadn't burned down.

Someone must have put it out.

She went in through the huge open door. It was dark inside, with the only light coming through the open door. The windows were black with smoke on one side and the others showed only the steel-grey sky that gave up snow. On the counter she saw what looked like a hurricane lamp. She pulled the chimney off, wound the wick upward, and lit it. It flamed high and fast, and she put the glass back on it. The smell was kerosene, but she wasn't familiar enough with that odor to recognize it. She left the lamp on the desk and moved around carefully. She walked up and down the rows, reading labels for chicken feed, pig feed, medicines for horse's hooves and long-rotted fifty pound bags of carrots. Rolls of chicken wire stood up in a bay and she thought about bringing some back to reinforce the house. She'd need to get a car running to carry it, but the roads in Eden were remarkably clear. She saw quickly that this was not the kind of place that would sell snowshoes or anything she needed. She went back for the hurricane lamp and picked it up gingerly, found the staircase that led up to the office.

The office was a little messy, with a thousand notes tacked up on the walls and the dead computer. She found map books marked with delivery routes for hay and feed, and stuffed two into her bag. The rest of the mess was invoices and phone numbers, nothing she could use. She headed back down.

She sat on the counter and ate some sardines she had packed for the trip. She flipped pages in the map book until she found where she was. Scanning the grid, she looked for any town big enough to have a shopping mall, a camping goods store, anything. She thought Huntsville, about six miles away, looked promising. When she had finished and looked long and hard at the route, she carried the lamp outside with her. She blew a few times before she managed to put it out. She thought she should take it with her. She did not think to pick up kerosene.

Around the back side of the store, a few cars sat parked. She knew cars that hadn't been driven in a year or so didn't start. One of these sat on clearly flat tires. Another had been a hay truck before, with tall guards on all sides to hold bales in. It looked too big to maneuver, and she decided against it. Parked closest to the wall was a little Honda. It was old, with manual locks and window cranks. She opened the passenger door and was stunned to see the keys in the ignition. She came around and let herself inside, setting the lamp carefully on the floor.

For a minute, she just breathed it in. The car smelled stale, like it hadn't been opened in all this time. In that stale smell was a lost world. Cologne and sneaked hamburgers and the plasticky aroma of car upholstery that has sat in the sun for a few years. The rubbery smell of the dashboard and the dirt and crumbs embedded in the carpet. Scent is the key to the door of memory. For a minute, she let herself live in it. The minute ended when the smell of the kerosene lamp made itself known. An intruder from the new world. She opened her eyes and looked around. Keys in the ignition, windows not broken.

Cautious hope began to spread in her chest. She reached for the keys and turned them slowly through the clicks. On the third, a set of needles iumped in the dash. Her heart jumped with them.

She cranked it all the way and the engine slugged and woke slowly, groaning. She backed off and did it again, it complaining nyeah nyeah nyeah as it tried to shake the cold and inaction of the last year. The battery wasn't dead. She knew that would sound like a dry click and nothing more. Nothing would light up or move. Cranked it again and this time stomped on the gas while doing it. The engine coughed, choked, caught, and then died. She waited one second before doing it again. It sputtered and guttered and then roared to life, her foot pouring gas into the injector.

She pounded the wheel triumphantly with her palms. The gas gauge read half full. She backed it up slowly and drove out onto the road. Fresh snow was all over everything, and she knew she'd have to go slowly. She wondered about the tires but did not get out to check. Rolling at a creeping pace, she eased out on the road in the direction of Huntsville.

It wasn't long before the noises set in. Knocking and whining, the car started to let her know that this couldn't last. The engine coughed and kicked, but she pushed on. If it was going to die, she wanted to ride it until it quit. She had gone nearly five miles when it stopped and wouldn't start again. She cursed at it a little, then got halfway out, put it in neutral, and rolled it to the side of the road. After it stopped moving, she looked at it and wondered why she had bothered. She looked up and down the snowy road, seeing black and white nothingness. No lines of cars honked behind her, no courteous country gentlemen hopped out of pickup trucks to offer assistance to the little lady. She could have left the car in the dead center of the road with all the doors open for all it mattered.

She thought for a minute about whether to grab the kerosene lantern from the floor of the car. She decided not to carry it, but that she would take this same road back, hopefully in another car or on a bike, and take it back home. She began to walk the last mile or so into Huntsville.

As soon as she got near town, she knew something was different here. At the outskirts, she began to see cows fenced in on suburban lawns in twos and threes, drinking out of kiddie pools and old bathtubs full of water. Each of the lawns had a shelter or a windbreak full of clean hay for the animals to escape the cold. For the most part, they seemed woolly for the winter and unbothered by the snow. In one yard, she heard the unmistakable gabbling of a chicken coop. She immediately knew that people were keeping these animals, probably a large group of them. She looked around, peering into the windows of the houses. She looked up and down each street for more signs of habitation. She listened hard through the snowy silence. Nothing.

She followed the road toward the center of town and the main drag. She knew there would be people there. She stopped at a bay window in the front of a tiny pink house and checked herself. She looked good, bundled up. She hadn't bothered to dirty her jaw in a few days, but she wasn't very clean, either. She touched the buttons of her coat and drew her scarf up, fluffing it to completely conceal her neck and part of her chin. She reached back and touched the butt of her gun. Calmed, she pulled the hem of her coat down over it. She turned back and kept walking into town.

When she reached Main Street, she saw the hub of activity. There was a tall church, with a steeple that had a lightning rod or a spike on the top. Beside it, a greenhouse had been built on top of what used to be the church parking lot. Dozens of men moved in and out through the door, talking with one another, gesturing. She couldn't hear them. The store she wanted was on the far end of the street. She could double back and come around the block behind it to avoid being seen. She stood motionless, deciding. It was too risky to meet them, she thought. She turned around to go back and wait until after dark to raid the store.

When she turned, she found herself almost face to face with a young man who had a blond beard and a generous smile.

"Welcome, brother!" He strode toward her, holding out his hand. "Where did you come from? We haven't had a refugee in months!"

Frozen for a moment, she was not sure what to do. She couldn't shoot this guy in the middle of town. She knew she was outnumbered. He wasn't threatening at all, and he had called her 'brother' and 'refugee.' Those were terms she could deal with.

Cautiously she put out her right hand. "Hi. I just came in from Eden."

"Eden? Heck, I'm from Eden, and I sure don't know you."

"Well, I just got to Eden. I'm from San Francisco."

"Wowie, that's a long trip. How'd you get all this way? Oh, never mind all the long story. Where are my manners? Are you hungry or hurt? Do you need anything?"

She studied his face carefully. He seemed totally sincere, right down to his fake swears. The moment felt surreal to her, like Disneyland tour guides showing up to lead her out of hell. "I'm ok. I need to get back to Eden, is all. My car broke down and-"

"Well, shoot, I'm sure someone could take you back to Eden, but why would you go back there? It's pretty deserted."

"I… I have all my gear there. I sort of set up camp."

"Hey, I'll let the elders talk to you about it, but I expect you'll want to stay here. We haven't had a new face in a long time. Why don't you let me walk you to the stake center and introduce you. Oh, what's your name, brother?"

"Dusty. I'm Dusty Jones."

He had held her hand this whole time, and now he pumped it enthusiastically up and down.

"Welcome to Huntsville, Brother Dusty. I'm Frank Olsen. I hope you'll at least stay for dinner. Come on, let me show you off to everybody."

He let go of her hand, but he put his on her shoulder instead. His hands were wide and square, with blond hair sprouting out of the back. His eyes were baby blue and as round as could be. The walk over to the church building he had called the 'stake center' was far too short for her liking.

Her heart was beating a little too fast and she breathed deep, trying to remember to talk low and slowly, like a man would. They reached the door where an older man stood like a cheerful guard.

"Hello there, Frank! Who's this young man?" The old man had eyebrows that seemed to reach all over his face, up and down in long bristles. They worked as he squinted to see her clearly.

"This is Brother Dusty. He just came in from Eden."

The man with the eyebrows reached out and shook her hand heartily. "Welcome! Better take him in the meet the elders."

Frank beamed. "That's my plan! Thanks, Brother Albert."

Albert opened the door and closed it behind them, back at his post. Inside the building was warm and bright. The hallways were spacious and clean and all the wood looked polished. The large bucolic paintings of Jesus that hung on the walls were freshly dusted. They walked past the open doors of a cavernous chapel space. As she passed, she could see the wall behind the dais was made up of river rock, all the way to the ceiling. No cross, no crucifix, just a podium.

"Here we are!" Frank rapped on a door three times and a teenage boy answered. "Hi, Brother Tyler. Are the elders in a meeting?"

"No, they're just getting ready to go to dinner. Say- is that a refugee?" He held out a hand to Dusty. She took it and let him pump her up and down, feeling very silly.

Frank spoke for her. "This is Brother Dusty, he just got in. Can I take him in to meet the elders?"

"Well, sure!" The kid got out of the doorway and gestured them in. Frank opened another door on the other side of the room. He stepped in ahead of her, and she followed.

It was a wide room, set with a very modern conference table surrounded by leather swiveling desk chairs in black. Seated around it were five men, all white with white hair, most with white beards. They all looked up as she and Frank came through the door.

"Elders, this is Dusty Jones. He's a refugee from San Francisco who just came in through Eden."

The man at the head of the table spoke up first. His voice was rich and resonant, though he looked to be nearly seventy years old. "Welcome, Brother Dusty. This is Huntsville, a survivor's colony and a stake of the Church of Jesus Christ of Latter-Day Saints."

"Oh." It popped out of her before she could think. "Mormons."

The men around the table were unmoved. Another spoke this time. "Yes, Mormons. We prefer to be called Latter-Day Saints, or LDS. But I'm sure in California many people say 'Mormon' instead."

The head man did not rise from his seat or offer a hand, but his smile was genial. "I'm Elder Comstock. This is Elder Sterling, Elder Graves, Elder Johannsen, and Elder Evans." They nodded in order as they were introduced. Dusty looked at each of them and tried to figure out how to tell them apart. Graves did not have a beard. Comstock was clearly in charge. The rest all looked alike, even wearing the same boring dark suits and bland ties. She looked at Frank out of the corner of her eye. She saw that he was dressed for work, but incredibly clean. His hair looked freshly trimmed, and he wasn't growing a beard for lack of equipment. He was neat. The old men around the table were the same: neat, clean, fastidious. For a moment, she thought she might be dreaming.

"Brother Dusty," Comstock was saying as she came out of her reverie. "We would like very much to hear about your journey, and any news you can tell us. Would you join us for dinner? We'd be honored to have a guest."

She nodded. "Sure, I… I can tell you what I know but it isn't much."

Comstock smiled, and it was such a grandfatherly smile that it made her glad to see it. "We've all heard each other's stories a thousand times. Even if it's a dull story, it will be delightful to hear something new."

She was just a little charmed. She was trying to get a read on these people, but everything confused her. They were too polite, too clean.

Don't they know the world ended?

She followed the line of them out the door, beginning to smell food. It smelled incredible.

Comstock led the line into an auditorium. The floor was wood laminate and it shone like a mirror. The room was set with round tables all over. Each table was spread with a cloth and silverware at each place. In the center were short round vases with glass beads in the bottom and silk flowers in the top. On the wall was a never-ending spread of art made by children. Clumsy crayon drawings and felt apples crowded against coloring pages and sticky construction paper collages. Malformed mommies and daddies beamed with huge smiles and waved with stick-fingers from picture after picture of sunny houses and blue skies.

The white beards reached a table and sat, gesturing to an empty seat for her. She sat, still staring around the room.

"Are there children-"

Dozens of men came streaming in through every door, talking and laughing and sitting at tables. She saw more than a few staring her way, and some sidebars as the word spread that there was an outsider present. She watched the gossip of her existence spread across the room, saw Frank Olsen enjoy a moment of minor celebrity as everyone confirmed the news with him. They quieted as they sat, and every face seemed turned toward her. She tried not to look back, but looked down at the gleaming steel flatware in front of her, laid out perfectly on the white plastic tablecloth.

The quiet let up as the doors to the kitchen opened. The smell of food came through, strong and sure it had to be spaghetti. Teenage boys came out loaded with serving bowls and made for the tables. Dusty's table was served last. The bowls were heaping with green salad, spaghetti tossed with marinara covered with meatballs, and another full of rolls that smelled fresh and yeasty and warm. She watched them go by, her mouth wet with anticipation.

Behind the team of teenagers delivering food, there came three women. One was young, maybe twenty. The next was in her thirties, motherly, with beautiful shining black hair. The last was perhaps a little older, gray at the temples, and dumpy in dress that covered her to the neck and ankles. Dusty stared at them as they approached her table, each bearing a bowl. They set them down with smiles. The youngest one was strawberry blonde and pretty in a hometown girl with no makeup sort of way. When she got close, Dusty saw she was sprinkled with freckles. After setting down the food, they walked decorously to their own table that they shared with two men and a couple of empty chairs.

Elder Comstock stood and folded his arms. People around the room stayed seated but folded theirs. Dusty did the same, thinking it was better not to stand out.

"Dear most gracious Heavenly Father," he intoned gently. "We thank thee for this day and for this food and the hands that prepared it. We ask that you bless it that it may strengthen and nourish our bodies…"

As the prayer went on, Dusty looked around the room. Every head was bent and every eye was closed. Even the teenage boys seemed reverent. She stared around at their perfect quiet, their unruffled stillness. She looked over to the table where the women sat. They seemed at ease and as involved in the prayer as any of the men. Before it ended, she bowed her head so as not to be caught.

"…in Jesus' name, Amen." As he finished speaking, before he could even fully sit down, the room broke into noise that mostly began with "please pass." Dusty held herself back and waited for the food to come to her. She made a pile of salad on her plate and laid an equally large helping of spaghetti beside it. She took a roll from the bowl and reached for a bottle of salad dressing that had arrived on the table when she wasn't watching. Elder Comstock was holding a small plate of fresh butter that he served himself from sparingly before passing it on.

"Butter is still in short supply, I'm afraid. We're working on milk production and we hope to start making cheese soon. But Sister Everly was able to make about a pound of sweet cream butter this month, and we're trying to make it last." The small plate reached her and she took a tiny sliver of it by knife to her still-warm roll. She put it straight into her mouth and the long-lost taste transported her. She set the rest aside to eat last.

The room buzzed with conversation and Dusty was glad to be ignored for a few minutes while she crammed hot food into her mouth. It had been so long since she'd eaten a real meal, food prepared by someone else with courses and a theme, so that she couldn't focus on anything else. The sauce was obviously straight out of a can. The pasta was overcooked and spongy. The salad dressing was shelf-stable uninspired processed junk. She didn't care. It was not served in a can or eaten alone and in haste. It tasted as good as anything ever had in her life, especially the bread. When she had cleaned her plate, she picked up the buttery remains and swiped the last of the red sauce up with it, reveling in every bite. When she finished, the strawberry blond girl had reappeared to pour her a glass of lemonade. It was terribly sweet, the kind made from powder, but it had been poured over a full glass of snow. Dusty thanked her and took long swallows from it. Another soon appeared.

"Well, sir." It was Elder Johannsen this time. "Why don't you tell us about yourself?"

As if on cue, the room quieted down. She thought for a moment before beginning.

"I was working as a PA in San Francisco when the plague started. We handled a lot of casualties, mostly women and children. When the government broke down, things got pretty terrible. I left the city as soon as I could and started moving east. I met a few people here and there, but mostly out on the road the ones you meet are monsters. It isn't safe out there."

Dusty saw the freckled girl didn't like that. All over the room, people looked uncomfortable.

"So, I've been traveling and offering medical assistance to people I meet who aren't killers. I found Eden and it was so deserted I couldn't figure out what had happened. I was hoping for some good winter gear, so I came to Huntsville, and here you all are."

Johannsen nodded. "Indeed, indeed. Here we are. Many of us are from Eden. I myself have a home there. Brother Jesperson, Brother Chalmers, and Brother Anderson, as well."

She cleared her throat. "I…uh… I've been staying in a house over there." She pulled the keys out of her pocket and looked at the tag on the key ring. "700 North 900 West, it's at the end of the street."

The man who had been pointed out as Brother Chalmers stood up. "That's Brother Westin's place. He died of the sickness. He'd be glad to know a traveler found some refuge at his house. You go ahead and take whatever you need from there."

"Um… thank you." She felt insanely awkward. Were they still expecting to enforce rules of ownership? Their whole society looked like pretense to her, like a stubborn conceit. Let's pretend we have a community, let's pretend nothing has changed. "Well, I want to get back to Eden tonight, if anyone knows an easier way than walking the six miles, I'd like to hear it."

Elder Johannsen was looking at her. "Tell us more about the people you met out there."

She shrugged. "Bands of men, mostly. There are almost no women anywhere. I've met a few guys who seemed alright, but all the others have been rapists and murderers."

The whole room seemed to tense. She tried to backpedal. "I hardly saw anyone, really. It's very deserted out there, I could go days without seeing anyone. Just when I did-"

Johannsen shushed her a little. "That's alright, brother. Don't dwell on it. No need to worry the children talking of such things. Sisters."

At his word, the three women stood up and went back to the kitchen. The teenage boys were sent right after them. They came back with huge bowls of Jell-O in every color, and laid them on the tables as before. Dusty helped herself to a large humped spoonful in bright green and began to eat it. Conversation began again around the room, but it was more subdued this time. The mention of children had made Dusty look around the room, as if she had missed them. She shook it off, not sure what he had meant.

Elder Comstock spoke to her. "Someone can drive you back into Eden, if that's what you want. But we'd like to offer you a place among us. We could use another man with medical skills. We have Brother Beaumont, but he's a dentist. You say you're a physician's assistant?"

"Yes, that's right. I specialized in obstetrics and gynecology."

Comstock nodded, pleased. "Stay here tonight, spend tomorrow with us. It's too dark to go back to Eden now, anyway. Let us try to convince you to join us. There's no need for you to be all alone over in Eden with all of us here. We'd much rather you stayed with us."

She couldn't think of a good way to leave, and she was tired. "Alright. No promises. But I will stay tonight."

He nodded as though there had been no doubt in his mind. "Wonderful. Brother Anderson?"

A young man a few tables away from them stood up and approached. "Yes, Elder?"

"Brother Dusty, this is Brother Chet Anderson. He'll be a missionary soon, won't you, son?"

"Yes, sir."

"Chet, this is Dusty. He's going to stay tonight with us. Can you put him in your companion's bed, since it's empty?"

"Yes, sir."

"Excellent. Dusty, Chet here will help you with anything you might need."

Comstock turned from them in wordless dismissal, speaking to Elder Johannsen. Dusty stood up to follow Chet. Around them, the women and boys were clearing the tables, bustling back into the kitchen. The whole system looked neatly organized, as if everyone knew his role without ever being told.

Chet was tall and thickly built, the sort of kid you would expect to play football. He was clean shaven and golden-blond. His eyes were small in his face and a brilliant green. His skin had no hint of acne whatsoever.

Handsome boy. Probably broke some hearts back when there were still hearts to break.

He led her to a small house close to the center of town and opened the unlocked front door. "This is the house I was sharing with my companion. The bathroom is good for washing, and there's a pot on the stove to heat up water. The toilet's useless, so there's a latrine trench out back. We'll have to dig a new one soon. Kitchen's there, bedroom's there." He pointed from the living room down the hallway.

"Who's… where's your companion?" She watched him as he sat down on a blue couch.

"My companion was Elder McCarthy. Bruce. We were supposed to go on a mission together.

One morning I woke up and he was just gone. He was my best friend."

She sat down next to him, leaving a whole cushion between them. "Oh. I had someone do that to me. It hurts. I'm sorry."

He sighed. "Yeah. I hope he's ok. Sometimes I think he just wanted to go find batteries for his Gameboy without getting caught."

She smiled at him. "Maybe that's it. So, are you from Huntsville? Or Eden?"

"I'm from Ogden. Some missionaries from Huntsville found me. I left home after my mother and sisters died. I wanted to go to Salt Lake, but they told me they had been there, and it wasn't a good idea."

"Why not?"

"They said part of town had been burned and there were gangs of guys on motorcycles riding everywhere. I can't imagine Salt Lake City full of motorcycle gangs, but I'll take their word for it. They brought me here, instead." He looked disappointed.

"Did you not want to come here?" She watched him closely. She wasn't sure they'd try and hold her, but she was anxious to hear what he said.

"No, I mean… I don't know. I wanted to be around people, is all. There sure are people here. I was just hoping…"

"What were you hoping?" He wasn't a prisoner. Just a kid.

"Hoping that all the girls hadn't died everywhere. Every family I knew in Ogden had daughters, more girls than boys. I had four sisters, I had a friend who had six. School seemed like it was mostly girls. The girls in my ward were brats with braces and they weren't even that cute. But I miss them so much, all of them. I keep hoping the missionaries will bring back a bunch of girls who just got lost, but they're ok and happy. But most of the guys who leave don't even come back." He sat with his arms curled in, palms of his hands turned up in his lap. His face pulled down at the corners and he looked old.

"I've seen girls." She said it quietly, but his head whipped toward her.

"Really?"

"Yeah, really. Not many, but they are out there. Girls your age, even. What are you, like eighteen?"

"Seventeen. As soon as they find me another companion, I'll be sent out." He didn't look excited.

"So what does that mean? You go out and… convert people?"

He laughed a little. "That's what missionaries used to do. Now all missions are service missions. We're sent out to find survivors and help them, bring them back if we can convince them to come. Lots of the people here came from around Ogden and Hyrum and Brigham City. But the guys that are sent far away…"

"They don't come back, right?" She leaned back on the arm of the couch, watching him.

"No. Anybody sent to Idaho or Nevada… nobody has made it back from those missions yet."

"Are they going out armed?"

He looked shocked. "No. We can only take our scriptures and a few things. Like the apostles. If we had guns, people might think we were dangerous."

They're not coming back. He knows that, he just doesn't want to believe it.

She blinked at him. "A lot of people out there have guns. The world is full of guns, you just have to find them. These guys… you might have a better chance if you found one."

He shook his head, sadly. "We're doing God's work. That's not the right tool for it."

"Ok. Good luck then. I hope you get sent to somewhere close."

He stood up. "I'll put on the kettle so you can have some hot water to clean up with." He walked into the kitchen, but she followed.

"How many of you are there here, now?"

"Fifty nine. Fifty two men, three women." He kept his back to her.

"That's fifty five. Are the other four trans?"

He looked over his shoulder. "What?"

"Who are the other four?"

"Oh." He turned back to the kettle. "The kids."

"I didn't see them at dinner. Where are they?" She walked up to stand beside the stove, to look at him. "Where are the kids?"

"They're kept away from everybody, as a precaution. They're the only ones who made it." His face was distracted, giving nothing away.

"Do you know them? Are they boys or girls?"

"Two boys, two girls. All under ten. The sisters take care of them, and they're in a special house. Everyone's afraid they'll get sick or hurt, or someone will try to take them. They have to be protected."

"Why? Why can't they be out in public?"

The fire in the stove caught and he put the kettle on the black iron top. "I'm never going to get married. Neither are you. Neither are any of the brothers here, unless the missionaries bring home girls. Those kids can marry each other, have kids of their own. Nobody can get in the way of that. They're the only thing we have that looks like a future."

His eyes blazed as the room warmed up. He closed the door to the little stove and stared her down, daring her to argue.

Hidden children. Flowers in the attic.

"Have any of the women here had babies in the last year?"

Blazing still, he did not look away. "Not yet. But they're all married, and it will happen. Children will be born in the covenant."

"Since I was working in gynecology, I can tell you that's going to be harder than it sounds. This sickness, this virus or whatever it was, seems to complicate pregnancy. Every pregnancy. I haven't seen a child born in more than a year who lived a day."

"God has not abandoned us. We're just being tested. We'll come through."

She watched him for any sign of doubt, for the melancholy doom that had crossed his face when he thought of his mission. She saw nothing but stubborn belief. "I hope you're right."

With a candle burning, she locked the door to the bathroom and stripped naked. She took the pot of water into the tub and carefully soaped from top to bottom, using the precious hot water to wash it all away. She washed her short hair and was shocked to look at all she had grown in her underarms. She'd been shaving there since she was thirteen. Her leg hair had come in long and dark, but fine. It felt so alien to be naked, she could not quite own or inhabit her body. It was becoming a stranger to her.

I used to live here.

The compression vest was yellowed and dingy with constant wear. She saved a little water when she was clean to soap and rinse it out, too. She hung it up on the showerhead after she had rung it out. She'd have to put it back on wet, but it was already much improved. She stepped out of the tub and stood on a clean towel, stiff from line-drying inside the house. In the candlelit mirror, she looked at herself for a while. She thought she looked older. Her breasts were smaller than she remembered. She thought that was the result of weight loss, but maybe constant compression had something to do with that, too. Her hair was a little shaggy. She thought someone could give her one of the smart side-parted cuts from the 1950s barber shop poster that everyone in Huntsville seemed to have.

She got the compression vest back on. Chet had given her a set of long underwear that were close to her size. She put them on and checked to see that the lights were out before crossing the room toward the bunk beds. Chet was on top and did not look up. She set up her clothes right beside the bed, she planned to put them on over the long johns. The bunk was narrow but the comforter was down-filled and the pillow smelled fresh and clean. She sunk right into it and fell into a dreamless sleep.

When she woke up, Chet was already up and dressed. It was still dark out.

"I've got seminary. Do you want to come?"

She sat up slowly, mindful of the top bunk overhead. "No, you go ahead. I'm going to get dressed and walk around a bit."

He shrugged with a brief grin. "Ok. See you later!" He bounded out the door like a big kid.

Dusty looked after him, thinking that he must be pretty used to such early mornings.

She got dressed quickly and went out the front door without locking it. She walked slowly back toward the center of town. Men were coming out of their doors and flipping up their collars against the cold. Many of them waved to her as they split off toward their day's work. She headed back to the stake center, where smoke was coming out of the chimneys. The door was open but no one was posted as guard this time.

She walked in through the long hallways, past the chapel and the paintings of Jesus. She headed through the auditorium to doors through which food had come the day before. She knew that back there somewhere was a kitchen.

Behind the swinging café doors, three women worked. They

were pulling long muffin trays out of a large wall oven and setting them down to cool on a wide gleaming stainless steel countertop. Dusty smelled cornbread. They looked up as she entered, but did not stop their work.

The oldest woman spoke up first, her hands still busy and her eyes on her task. "You're not allowed to be back here, stranger."

"I'm sorry," Dusty said. "I just didn't get the chance to speak with any of you yesterday."

The woman with the gray at her temples set down her corn muffins and put her hands on her hips. "I'm Sister Everly. This is Sister Johannsen and Sister Obermeyer. And I'm afraid that's all the speaking we're going to do without our husbands present." She gave Dusty a pointed look and went back to her work.

"Forgive me ladies, I meant no disrespect." Dusty managed this very formal apology without missing a beat, despite it feeling like an antique phrase out of the attic of her brain. She turned to leave.

Sister Obermeyer, the young one with the strawberry blonde hair, called after her. "Breakfast is in less than an hour. See you soon!"

Dusty saw herself out and went back into the large auditorium. She walked the walls looking at the children's pictures. Many of them were colored and filled-out pages of activity books. Others were freehand drawings, but Dusty thought they were probably directed by an adult. Every picture had four examples of the same thing, and every single one was rosy and happy and envisioned a perfect world. If children of the plague were allowed to draw what they felt, Dusty imagined the room would look different.

But all of the children's pictures had smiling mommies in them.

She was still moving around the room when the three women emerged from the kitchen, green tablecloths in their hands.

"Can I help?"

Sister Everly pursed her lips. "Well, we always run a little behind while the boys are at seminary. I suppose you can." She broke her stack of them in half and handed them over to Dusty. Dusty moved about efficiently, grabbing them by their edges and flipping them out over the tables. Coming to the last cloth, she saw that all the others had finished and were bustling back through the swinging doors.

Sister Johannsen came back out first. Her shining black hair was done up in braids that looked elaborate and difficult. She was carrying two centerpieces.

"So, are you Elder Johannsen's wife?"

She did not look up, but laid her two centerpieces and kept moving. "I'm his daughter in law."

She went back through the doors.

Can't one of them hold still for five minutes and talk to me?

Sister Everly was next, with four centerpieces held together in her hands like a practiced waitress carries drinks.

"I don't believe I've met your husband, ma'am."

Sister Everly looked at Dusty, but did it with the kind of look a woman gives a troublesome vacuum cleaner. "Mr. Everly sat beside me at dinner last night. He's a farmer."

"Oh, I saw the chickens and cows on the edge of town."

"My husband farms peas and beans. He's in charge of them year-round."

"How nice," Dusty said to the swinging doors.

Sister Obermeyer came out with four centerpieces, carrying the way Sister Everly had. "And what does your husband do?"

Her brows furrowed a little and her pink mouth flattened. "He's a missionary. Serving in Colorado."

"How long has he been gone?"

"Five months. They're due back like any day now." She disappeared again.

The two older women emerged together, and Dusty was not yet ready to give up. "Where are the children? Are any of them yours?"

"Yes," said both women.

"I'd love to meet them. I haven't seen a child in a long time. I have experience treating children, if they need any medical help. I'd love just to hear stories about them." Dusty had years of experience talking to mothers. Patients and nurses alike couldn't stop themselves from telling these stories, showing their pictures, or sharing their worries.

Sister Everly was as stony-faced as ever, but Sister Johannsen softened around the eyes. "You can't meet them," the younger woman said. "They're kept separate. But I could tell you-"

"You could, when your work is done. Mind yourself, Anne. Come along now." Sister Johannsen looked back at the older woman like a child who was promised a treat and then denied it. She followed meekly, however.

Dusty sighed, exasperated. She flopped into one of the chairs and let them buzz around her, laying silverware and making last minute preparations for breakfast. When the men began filing in, Dusty watched and sat at the table with the largest number of empty seats, intending to sit with the women when they finished. She noticed she got a few sharp glances, but she wasn't told to move. She patiently folded her arms for prayer and sat politely passing food and waiting for conversation to begin. The couples at her table served one another scrambled eggs and corn muffins and steamed broccoli.

When she thought it was safe to try again, she went back to work on Sister Johannsen. "So, tell me about your children."

Her husband looked up, shocked. "Our two boys died during the sickness, Brother."

"But your wife said some of the children here were hers."

He frowned at her. "The Law of Consecration doesn't really make them ours, honey. They're still sealed to their own folks."

The law of what now?

She smiled at him and it made her beautiful. "Sure they're ours. They're everyone's! There's Patty, that's the oldest. She's a beautiful little girl, nine years old. She loves to sing and draw pictures. I'm reading Where the Red Fern Grows with her right now and she wants a puppy so bad. Then there's her sister Mikayla, who's very strong willed and stubborn. She's just seven and she loves Barbies. She's got dozens, but we had to sort through Barbie's clothes to find some that were modest." She giggled a little here, her eyes alight. "Then the boys, Ben and John. Ben's seven, too, and John is six. They're both so smart, already reading and writing and Ben can name all the books of the Old Testament in order. John is very shy and affectionate. He's a cuddly one! I wish I had pictures. The sisters and I all teach them and care for them. They're having their breakfast now, too, with Jodi."

"Jodi?"

"Sister Obermeyer. It's her day to eat with them." Sure enough, the youngest woman was missing from the table.

The redhead. Right.

Brother Johannsen was still clearly uncomfortable, but he was pleased with his wife. "Anne was a wonderful mother. I'm glad she's helping to care for the stake's children. But soon enough she'll have my baby to take care of. I guess I'm just a little selfish that way. I want my own boys back, and I can't wait to have our own again."

"Of course, sweetheart." They gazed at each other with a syrupy sweetness that Dusty could not believe was real. She decided to change the subject.

"So I'd like to get my hair cut. Can any of you tell me who does all these neat cuts?"

Brother Everly pointed with a forkful of egg to another table. "Brother White. He cut hair for the navy for fifteen years. Just ask him, he'll fix you up."

Dusty finished off her corn muffins and excused herself from the table. She walked over to Brother White and made arrangements for a haircut right after breakfast.

Brother White sat her in an old barber's chair in his kitchen. The house was dead quiet. His tools were laid out on a clean white towel. His shears were very old-looking, with mother of pearl handles. She told him she thought they were handsome.

"They were a gift from my mother, when I got assigned to barbering by the navy. She said I needed something with a little class. Just the standard cut?"

"Sure, I just want it cleaned up and off my neck."

"Shave, too?" He grabbed her by the chin, rubbing a little with his thumb. The sudden contact shocked her and she jerked her head away.

"No!" She settled back down as fast as she could. "No. I don't grow much facial hair. Or much chest hair. My father didn't, either. Just lucky."

The old barber seemed unruffled. "My beard keeps my face warm." He combed her hair out with a wet brush and started cutting.

"So is there a sporting goods store in Huntsville? I'd like to get some snowshoes or better boots, if I can."

"Sure, sure. There's a Cabella's that I'm sure will have something. You'll have to ask the bishop about it though."

"The bishop?"

"Elder Comstock. Bishop Comstock. You'll just need

permission to take something from the bishop's storehouse."

"What's the bishop's storehouse?"

His cold steel scissors slid along the back of her neck in a perfect straight line. "It's everything that belongs to the town. He's in charge of making sure that people get what they need."

Of course.

"Alright, I can do that. Where would he be around now?"

"Probably over to the courthouse. He'll be busy, though. All finished."

He pedaled the release to drop her back to the floor. She slid down on a cushion of air and he handed her a mirror. She took it and looked.

"Without a beard you look like a little boy," Brother White laughed. "Or a grownup tomboy."

"Thanks." Dusty patted the stray hairs off her shirt and walked out the kitchen door.

The courthouse was located at the opposite end of Main Street from the stake center. It wasn't a grand civic affair with columns or a dome, just a small-town courthouse. Plate glass in front with cement pillars to prevent an angry someone from driving through the façade. Useless metal detectors stood beside every entry point and the freshly-laundered American flag stood on an eagle-topped pole in the corner of the foyer.

A guard stood posted at the inner door, another bearded old white man and she started to feel very tired of seeing the same face. He let her pass.

Bishop Comstock was sitting on the judge's bench wearing the same dark suit. He was listening to a man standing in front of him tell a long whining story about a series of books he wanted to read that the other man in the room had not finished yet and wouldn't give up.

"I got to read the first half of the first book, and then he got permission to take the whole series. I don't want the whole series, just the first couple when he's done with them."

The man standing on the other side shook his head, his short dark curls shining in the sunlight that came through the windows. Snow had stopped falling and the day was cold, but bright. "I told him, I want to keep the whole series until I've finished them all. What if I need to go back and look something up? I don't want to have to track him down to get it back. I'll finish soon, and then he can have them."

Bishop Comstock looked thoughtfully down on them. "What are these books called? What are they about?"

The two men looked at one another, and then quickly away. The light-haired man spoke first.

"They're about a… a spy. A female courtier who spies… for a queen."

The man with the dark curls nodded.

The bishop looked from one to the other, understanding dawning on his face. "Are you brothers following the admonition of Paul? Would you say that this material is in keeping with covenants you made when you accepted the rights and responsibilities of the priesthood?"

Both men stared down at their shoes. "I want to withdraw my complaint," said the lighter man.

"It doesn't matter. We can work it out."

The bishop drummed his fingers on the desk. "I see. Would you say that this book is virtuous, lovely, of good report, or praiseworthy? I know you both and I think you're both better than this. Turn the books in to the elders at the stake center after dinner tonight. Neither one of you needs them." He tapped his gavel lightly and dismissed them with a look.

Dusty wasn't sure if there was an appointment system or a way to ask to be heard, so she just walked up the center aisle to stand before the bench.

"I was told to ask you about snowshoes."

Comstock looked up and then down at her. "What's that?"

"I came to Huntsville looking for snowshoes or other winter gear. The barber told me there was a Cabella's somewhere in town, but that I'd have to ask you. So here I am. Asking."

Comstock took an old-fashioned pocket watch out of his blazer and looked at it. Then he pulled on his overcoat. "Brother Dusty, will you take a walk with me? I don't have any more cases to hear today."

"Sure."

They walked together, quietly. Bishop Comstock led away from the courthouse, down one of the residential streets in town that Dusty hadn't seen yet. Covered with snow on a clear day, the houses looked cheery and well cared-for. They also looked empty. Dusty thought about empty houses in little towns like this all over the world, with men going and gone and no women left inside. Houses without housewives. No cooking and cleaning, no humming and apron-wearing wives and mothers like in the old sitcoms. No rushing minivans driven by lithe women in yoga pants whose children were well-behaved and spoke Mandarin. No soap-opera addicted overweight neglectful trailer trash with a dozen kids running around screaming, their mouths always stained with Kool-Aid. Every man in Huntsville remembered another life, expecting to come home every day to find someone there. All the empty houses sat. No one numbered the silent days.

Comstock walked with his hands clasped behind his back. His chin was down near his chest and his white beard made him look very solid, like a block of ice. His brow furrowed.

"Brother Dusty, you seem like a sensible man. May I be frank with you?"

She crossed her arms and looked at him as they kept walking. "Please."

"I'm glad you came to Huntsville. We need a little excitement here and there, and we certainly need a reminder that there are other people out in the world."

She didn't see a reason to respond to this. She could tell he was working up to something.

"The plain fact is we are not looking for more young men. The reasons must be obvious. We are especially not looking for young men who are not of our faith. We have a delicate balance here, with very few women and a lot of frustrated and upset brethren who aren't married. Do you follow me?"

"I follow, yes. Frankly, I don't know that I would stay even if I was wanted. I'd prefer to be on my own, back in Eden, until I'm ready to move on."

Comstock nodded, a short dip of his head into his beard, but kept his gaze down.

"I'd like to know that you're there through the winter, in case we need another medical man. You're not too far to get someone to you, even in the worst weather. A few men here have snowmobiles. Would you be alright with that?"

"Of course." She was thinking fast, trying to figure out how she'd deal with visitors without warning. "I'd… It'd be good to have a warning. Have you got flares, or a crank siren? So I could be ready when they arrive?"

"I'm sure we can find something." Comstock was looking at her a little oddly. She frowned and looked ahead, trying to seem concerned with practicality.

"So, I'll be heading back to Eden, then. Any chance of snowshoes or other useful gear to get me there?"

"Slow down, son." Comstock gave her a warning look. "No need to take off half-cocked. I want to make sure everyone knows this is your choice. With all the gossip about you-"

"Gossip? I've been here one day."

"Now, Brother Dusty, you know women can't help but gossip. The relief society told everyone you were flirting with them, asking questions when their husbands weren't around, trying to help with kitchen work." He smirked a little.

"I wasn't! I was just-"

"Oh, it's only natural, son. We all want to spend as much time around the sisters as we can. I understand that. I just don't want anyone to think anything improper happened and that you hied out of town."

How was I flirting? I made the most polite conversation I know how. Feel like I stumbled into Saudi Arabia.

"Uh-huh," she said noncommittally.

"So, here's the plan. I'd like you to stay one more night. Have lunch with the ward, stick around for missionary assignments. Have dinner, stay another night with Elder Anderson, and in the morning I'll have one of the brothers take you back by snowmobile. How's that sound?"

"That's fine." She gave up on the idea of snowshoes. Comstock wanted to be able to come to her, but didn't care for the idea of her being able to cross back into Huntsville during the winter.

She liked him a little less, but she understood.

"Good. Now that's settled, you may do as you like for the rest of the day. I'm going to drop by the greenhouse and watch the work there, if you'd like to walk with me." He made a left turn at the next street and she followed.

"Bishop Comstock, what were things like here when the plague got going?"

His hands let go behind his back. His bearing changed. He seemed to be drawing into himself, shrinking. "We're very isolated here."

She waited.

"We received instructions from Salt Lake while we could still communicate with them. The first presidency was very clear about preserving the ward and administering the sacrament and ordinances as usual. President Duncan spoke prophecy confirming that the plague would pass and children would be born again in the covenant if we had faith and were patient. There were instructions to ward presidents and bishops like me, and to all holders of the priesthood… but then nothing. Everything shut down. Many people fled for parts more remote than these. And so many died, so many. We tended to them, and some of us lived. So we obeyed. And we have been blessed. If we continue to obey, we will continue to be blessed."

The talk about hierarchy went past Dusty, who did not know this church well. She understood the gist of what he was saying. They had been lucky here. He believed their luck would hold out.

"What happened to Chet's friend? Do you know? Have there been many disappearances?"

Comstock stopped in the street, his boots crunching on churned-up snow. "You're talking about Elder McCarthy." He gave her a hard look.

"I think that was the name. Chet said he just disappeared one night. Do you lose a lot of people that way?"

He turned away from her to look at the greenhouse at the end of the lane. He clasped his hands behind his back again. "A few, yes."

She waited, but he did not elaborate.

"Did you send out search parties?"

Comstock looked deeply uncomfortable. "We did. Of course we did."

She was mystified, watching him for signs. "A lot of your people are locals, they must know the area. Where could these people be going? Do they just want to find another community?"

He looked at her quickly, appraising her. He looked at his shoes again. "We've found… some of them."

She struggled for a minute, not sure what to say. "Oh. Suicides."

She waited for him to confirm it or deny it. He did neither.

*Shit, he can't even say it.*

"That's happening everywhere. You know that, right? Living this way is hard, people are going to opt out."

Comstock breathed in quickly as if to speak, but nothing came out. He stared at her.

"You should tell Chet," she pressed him. "He needs to know it's over. Everyone does."

"No." He shook his head, not looking at her. "No. That's not how we've chosen to handle this issue."

He doesn't want anyone to know. Bad for leadership, bad for morale. Unsustainable.

"How many?"

"It's not important. It's going to stop the minute we find just one more woman or girl out there. That will be enough to bring hope. She will come. She was promised to us."

She wanted to get as far away from him as she could. "Enjoy the greenhouse. I'm going back to the stake center."

He smiled again, reverting back to his public persona. "I'll see you later, then." He turned away from her and walked toward the greenhouse with a jaunty step. She watched him for a moment before going back the way they had come.

In the stake center, the women were bustling as always, preparing lunch. Dusty didn't try engaging them this time. She sat and watched.

Jodi Obermeyer spoke to her first. "Don't you want to help us?"

She arched an eyebrow at the younger woman. "Wouldn't want anyone to think I was flirting."

Jodi blushed. In her fair freckled skin it was like the rising of mercury in a thermometer. She hurried back into the kitchen.

Sister Everly appeared in her place. "Brother Dusty, I heard you liked my rolls yesterday."

"That was amazing. I haven't had bread in a while, or butter. It was really something."

She nodded approvingly. "You're so thin! I wish I could butter you up all winter, but I'm afraid there's no more of that. Still, there will be more rolls at dinner tonight. They're rising now."

"Thank you. That'll be nice, since I'm leaving in the morning."

"Oh, so soon?" She looked crestfallen.

"Yes, I want to be back in Eden. I prefer to be on my own. But I'll be close by."

"Oh." She turned sadly and walked back into the kitchen.

Dusty watched the women set the tables without speaking again. Men filed in like figures in a cuckoo clock, right on time. She didn't try to sit with the women this time. She chose a random table and sat with her fingers woven together against her forehead. She stayed that way through the prayer.

Lunch was shepherd's pie and it was rich and heavy and meaty and delicious. The men at her table ate quickly, taking seconds happily, talking very little. Dusty was glad, she wasn't interested in talking. She did as they did and enjoyed another helping. When the dishes were cleared, Elder Graves stood and held his hands up for silence. The only beardless leader, he somehow seemed much older than the others. His face was deeply lined and he had the shrunken appearance of a tall man who has been pulled downward by time and work and sadness.

When the room quieted, he began to speak, gently. "As you all know, all our recent missionaries have returned except the last two. Elders Langdon and Obermeyer were assigned to Colorado to serve a mission. They have not returned on the appointed date, but we know they will be back soon, with the help of Heavenly Father."

Across the room from him, Sister Obermeyer put her face in her hands and started to cry.

Graves cleared his throat. "Despite the setbacks we have experienced, we know that the directive to complete a mission is still asked of us, and we must fulfill it. We know this to be true with every fiber of our being. So today, we call forth six new missionaries to serve."

The room tensed up. She swept her eyes across the faces around her, looking for Chet. He was there, pink in the cheeks with his eyes full of fear. The moment seemed to stretch out for a long time before Graves spoke again.

"Elder Cubner and Elder Grim."

Two young men rose from the same table and waited.

"You are called to Flagstaff, Arizona."

They both sat down again, slowly.

"Elder Behr and Elder Smith."

A fat teenager arose at Dusty's table and another across the room joined him. The other missionary seemed older, maybe twenty-five.

"You are called to serve in Albuquerque, New Mexico."

The older man sat down fast, disappearing from view. The chubby kid sunk slowly, his lower lip quivering. No one near him touched him or looked at him or said a word.

"Elder Anderson and Elder Flint. You are called to serve your mission in Billings, Montana."

Chet had stood with his back to her and she couldn't see his face. The tension in the room relaxed slightly.

"All those who will sustain these brothers in their callings, please indicate by the uplifted hand." Comstock looked out over the room and everyone lifted their right hands as though they were taking an oath. Dusty, startled, didn't move. She didn't understand what she was seeing. She watched Jodi Obermeyer raise her hand, still sobbing.

"We believe that Heavenly Father will protect you and help you reach your intended destination. We believe that you will render aid along the way out of the goodness of your hearts. We believe that you will meet women and children and offer them succor. We believe you can lead those who belong here back to Zion. We believe you will return with honor."

Jodi Obermeyer sobbed aloud.

Graves ignored her. "The missionaries will leave tomorrow, so tonight will be their farewell dinner. Let us all show them love and kindness and keep them in our prayers."

The women had shushed Sister Obermeyer and taken her back into the kitchen. Dusty did not see her at dinner.

There was an announcement during dessert that Brother Dusty had been allowed to go homesteading in Eden, but he would stay available for medical help if needed. He would be taken home by Brother Chalmers in the morning, and they were to wish him well. Dusty raised a hand to them but didn't speak. She didn't care. She was ready to go. Afterward, when the room began to empty out,

Dusty headed straight for Chet's house.

She reached it before him and let herself in. She found her bag where she had left it, but the house spotlessly restored to order. She waited, pacing.

Chet walked through the door minutes later, with another boy his age.

"Chet."

"Brother Dusty, this is Elder Flint. And I'm Elder Anderson now. You heard."

"I did. I need to talk to you." She cut her eyes toward Elder Flint.

Chet shrugged. "He can't leave. We have to stay within sight of each other for the next six months. Whatever it is, you can say it to us both."

"Fine." She sat down in a chair and gestured to them to sit on the couch.

"You're going to die out there." They both blanched. Elder Flint flushed and wouldn't look at her. She pressed on. "There are terrible people out there, and even if there weren't, it's cold as hell in Montana. You could get injured or freeze to death or meet up with wolves. Without weapons you guys will get picked off by whatever comes along."

"It's our duty to serve," Flint said dully, looking at nothing.

"Bullshit."

Chet started.

He has to see the situation. The logic is so simple.

"Look, there are too many men here, and not enough women. Didn't it occur to you that the elders are trying to get rid of you?"

Chet looked hurt. "Why would they do that? All we have is each other."

"Because sooner or later you're going to fight over the women. There will be affairs. Unless more women join you, it's inevitable. The elders are just trying to even up the score."

Flint was shaking his head. "They're not, that's not true. They want us to bring back survivors Anyone we can find, even men."

"For what? So you can all farm and build and send out missionaries until you just die off? What's the point of that?"

"The point is to do what God wills. That's all." Chet was angry now.

She tried to calm him down. Gently, she said, "Look, there are empty houses all over the place. Walk to another town and pick one. Settle in for six months. Be careful, sleep in shifts, watch each other's backs. Then pick up and come home, say there was nothing in Billings, and you're off the hook."

Flint looked outraged. "We won't lie. We won't come back with nothing."

They don't know. They haven't really seen what it's like out there, and there's no way to tell them.

"You're not going to come back at all." She was sure that no one sent more than maybe fifty miles away was ever going to come back. Not unless they armed themselves or avoided people at all costs.

Chet stood up. "It's stupid to argue. It's done. Now that I have a new companion, you'll have to sleep on the couch. Goodnight." He walked to the bathroom and closed the door. Flint rose to head into the bedroom and she tried one more time.

"You're not coming back, Flint. Has anybody sent that far out come back?"

His eyes were gray with thick lashes. When they finally looked into hers, she saw how flat and lifeless they were. He had already given up. The elders had likely given Chet another suicide.

"So? Maybe there's no one out there. Maybe the plague will come back here. What does it matter? Die here, die there. Die now, die later. Might as well go." He didn't wait for an answer. He didn't look back. She saw him go in and climb onto the top bunk in the semidarkness. The sound of Chet washing up came through the bathroom door.

She gave up. She wasn't sure why she had tried in the first place. There is no argument to be had with faith.

She lay on the couch, fully clothed, and waited for sleep. Sometime after Chet had gone wordlessly to bed, it came.

The snowmobile arrived in the morning with the brisk chopping sound of a brand-new motor. Brother Chalmers sat astride it and called out to her when she opened the door. She looked over her shoulder and saw that Anderson and Flint were already gone. She picked up her pack and went out the door.

Chalmers offered her a helmet and goggles and she took both. She was glad for her long underwear as they got underway, but by the halfway point the wind had cut through to her skin. It had begun to snow again, lightly. They passed her abandoned car on the road. She tried to point it out to him, but they couldn't hear one another at all. She was worried about riding behind Chalmers, about having to press herself into his back for stability as they rode. He wore a puffy goose-down jacket and she gave all the distance that she dared. He didn't notice anything unusual and she tried to put it out of her mind.

She was relieved to get away from Huntsville. What had seemed charming about the community when she arrived had quickly started to suffocate her. It was hard to be an outsider in so many ways. She worried about staying anywhere, with anyone too long. Eventually, like the barber, they would have questions. Make guesses. She would be found out.

When they reached the house she had chosen, she was relieved to see it untouched and very much the same as she had left it. Chalmers shook her hand by way of goodbye. "We're just up the road if you need us."

She nodded and pumped his hand. He took her goggles and helmet and stuffed them in his backpack before taking off. She let herself in and immediately set about lighting a great big fire. The silence stung at first, but she relaxed into it as the house began to warm up. She curled up on the sofa she had pulled in front of the fireplace, put her right hand on the gun in her belt, and fell asleep.

# Chapter Six

*???*

Winter. Maybe October. Think it's not December yet. Haven't seen the stars in a couple of weeks since it's always cloudy, but even then I couldn't guess the date. Days short nights long.

Left the Mormons about a week ago. Paranoid at first, checking the windows all the time, waking up thinking I heard something or someone. Just nerves. They're not coming. Don't think they would even if they needed help. Bandaged broken pregnant I fucking doubt it. Rather keep to their own. Fine by me.

Quiet = awful. Next chance I get I'm going to load up on batteries and an old tape deck or a CD player or something. A crank-operated Victrola would do. Sing and talk to nobody and it's always quiet. La la la even a song I hate pounding out of a jukebox would be perfect right now. Snow keeps everything silent outside. Used to leave the cooking channel on while I cleaned the house, just for the background noise. Three cups of chirp chirp stir in cups of giggles add a cookbook and a glossy headshot and bake for an hour while we pretend nothing will ever go wrong. Used to wish for quiet, to wake up when a garbage truck went rattling through the alley or when sirens whoop whoop down the street or a drunk stumbled and bellowed by my apartment window. Too much quiet, now. Pushing on me all the time.

Time I spent in Huntsville feels surreal. Church suppers and invisible children and five Santa Clauses talking bullshit about missions and prophecies. If they had gotten the electricity back on and were growing chocolate I wouldn't have stayed. Too weird and they'd have eventually figured me out.

No books in this house. No shitty paperbacks, no self-help no romance no fairy tales nothing. The bible, the Book of Mormon and a couple others of their texts I've never read. Hope it doesn't come to the Bible. Not up for the end times. They were wrong about it anyway. Tried the Book of Mormon. Can't get past the provenance in the first pages. Nope. Maps from the feed store don't have a library marked here in Eden. That leaves raiding houses for books. Eventually the boredom will get to me and I'll go out when there's a break in the snow. Been snowing for days. White white white down down down.

*Winter*

No break in the snow. Done a billion pushups. Found a wide door frame in the house where I can do pull ups. Never could do those before. Working out and singing old songs to myself. Thinking about Roxanne, about Chicken, about Jack. Too much.

Remember when Jack first started at the hospital, when we couldn't stand each other. He was too good looking, I swear he got highlights that summer. Told people I thought he was gay, but I really just hoped he was. Didn't want to get shot down. He was so out of my league. A good looking anesthesiologist walks in and every woman- from the pathologists to the CNAs fall into his lap. Wasn't gonna be me.

Remember trying to shut him up, shut him down. I knew I was smarter than him on the first day and I made sure he knew it, too. Made sure he couldn't keep up in conversation. Kept him out. Reminded people about inside jokes while he was around so he'd always be on the outside. When he dated Carly I made a few choice remarks about how she was just about his speed. It was catty. Shitty. But she always was the last to catch on. She went back to her ex, anyway. She always did.

Seemed like it was always like that. He was dating someone else, I was dating someone else. I ran into him one night while I was out with Leah, and he looked at me like he had it all figured out. Yeah you know me and so do all the ladies. You know me know me know me all the way down know me Jack I know you. Asked him out the next day, just to fuck with him.

But he said yes. Yes he said yes he said yes I said yes. All our life = yes.

Too much too fast and I knew I was in too deep. He always managed to surprise me. He was funny and sweet and kind of a goofball. I thought good looking guys defaulted to asshole, not trying to be much more than they had to. Living together just seemed like the best answer, since we both worked so much. We didn't have a lot of time together but just the weight of him beside me, just his smell and his snoring made a difference to my life. My life + Jack = better. Life + plague – babies + bullshit + guns – women + snow - Jack – sense – meaning + 5ccs depo provera administer over time results inconclusive. Lost the chart.

* * * * *

She sat over her diary, lost in it for a long time. When she could snap out of her reverie, she got up, got dressed for travel, and slung a rifle over her shoulder. It was still snowing and the wind had buried the front door in a three foot drift. She went around to the back of the house, sheltered from the wind, and went out. She walked the mile gap to the nearest neighbor, broke in, and started looking for something to occupy her mind.

Five hours later, with the last of the light, she made it back. She was dragging a sled behind her.

* * * * *

Fourteen books. Two iPods that I left behind for obvious reasons. One battered discman and five batteries, none of them the right size. But maybe if I keep looking. A basket of knitting and a booklet on how to do it. Never knitted in my life. Got invited to stitch 'n bitch a thousand times but it sounded pointless to me. Right now it sounds like an excellent idea.

Was really glad there aren't any houses nearer but now I realize that raiding anything is going to be an all-day affair. Only hit two and I can't go back out again soon. Want a fucking snowmobile.

Firewood is going slow. At least it's good stuff, fallen hardwood and not a bunch of pine. Burns for a long time.

Wish I had an almanac. Wish I had the SF public library. Wish I had the right batteries for this CD player, even if the only thing I have to listen to is this Destiny's Child CD in it. Wish I had a prime rib and a chocolate cake. Wish I had Netflix. Wish I had a friend. Wish I had Jack. Wish into the fire burn it like a djinn. Wishes into the fire. Fire.

* * * * *

She had been completely alone for twenty-seven days. She had read every book she could find and failed twice to try to start knitting a scarf. After the second attempt, she threw the bag out into the snow and watched it get buried. She sat at the window, scowling.

She was purely miserable. She slept long and late and ate listlessly, when it occurred to her. Her hair was growing out, she could feel it on the back of her neck. It had always grown fast. Every day she debated with herself what risks were the smarter ones to take. Stay here, take off the binder, be comfortable and take long baths. Re-read the books she had liked. No one was coming. She could walk around the house naked if she wanted.

She had spent a few hours outside, practicing to shoot the rifles. She found that she preferred the bolt action to the larger caliber break-action, although it had a scope, which she kept it in mind in case she needed to take a long shot. She felt competent and didn't want to waste ammunition, so she quit.

When she was lonely, she tortured herself with the idea that it could be worse. She thought of the men at the lake house, the men in the mall. She thought about getting caught in Nevada and living out her days on a chain, burning inside. She thought about her apartment in San Francisco and could come up with not a single memory before she killed a man in her own bed. There was no before. The world had always been ending.

She had stopped talking. She had stopping singing, humming, whistling. She felt like a wild animal, like a raccoon that had cleverly burrowed into a house for the winter. She was a silent, thoughtless thing. Nothing interested her. Out of habit or stubbornness, she didn't change her clothes or take that long indulgent bath. She reversed her sleeping cycle, staying up all night and sleeping all day. It snowed all the time.

She woke up one afternoon to the sound of pounding at the front door. Her heart was instantly in her throat, beating so swiftly she could barely breathe. She leapt up off the bed and picked up the rifle in the doorway. She came to the door and checked the peephole.

Outside was all white. A darker shape was buried halfway in snow, its face wrapped in dark cloth, unseen. The pounding started again, and with it a high-pitched voice.

"Please!"

She thought for a second and came to the idea that someone coming to surprise her wouldn't knock on the door. She set the rifle down but close enough to reach and tripped the locks.

The visitor stumbled forward and snow scattered across the floor of the entryway. The scarf pulled open and a woman's face appeared. Scared, cold, breathing steam and crying hot tears stood Jodi Obermeyer.

"Oh thank god you're still here. Thank god. Thank god. Thank god." She flung her arms around the startled woman's neck and hung there, sobbing. She slid free after a minute. "I was afraid you had gone. I didn't know where else to go."

Dusty dragged the woman close to the Franklin stove in the kitchen and made her sit down. She built up the fire until it leapt.

She watched Jodi trying to warm up, pulling off her snow-covered outer layers and scooting closer to the fire.

So beautiful. So rosy freckled pink. That special stupid is stealing over me…I am dumb around beautiful women. Seen the same thing happen to men. It's the kind of stupid that makes us pay attention to what a beautiful woman says, whether or not it's true or useful or sane. So glad to see somebody, once I got over the scare. If I was going to get surprised by someone at my door, I'm glad it was her.

When Jodi had warmed up enough, she started talking. "I know I shouldn't be here and I know if anyone finds out they'll think I've broken my vows, but I had to get out of Huntsville. I left while everybody was asleep. I know the way, somebody mentioned you were in the Westin house. But I've never walked this far alone before. It took me forever but I was afraid to stop because I thought I might freeze to death."

"You're lucky you didn't get lost."

"I know. But I didn't have any choice."

"Why don't you sit down on a chair and I'll make some tea and we can talk it over?"

Jodi stood up. "I don't drink tea." Standing, with her coats off and her long skirts falling to the floor, she was obviously pregnant.

"Oh shit."

Jodi put a hand protectively over her belly. "Is that any way to talk about a baby?"

"Oh shit," she repeated, unable to say anything else. She stepped forward with her hands out, instinctively wanting to touch.

Jodi walked away, cradling her abdomen and sitting down gently on the couch. "I didn't come here for you to lay hands on me. I'm still a married woman. Obviously."

"I'm sorry, I should have asked you, of course. It's just my training. I've treated pregnant woman for most of my professional career, I only wanted to assess…" She lost what she had been meaning to say.

Jodi's face crumpled in and she started to sob. "Everything is so horrible. I need to know that I can trust you. Please just…"

She walked over to face the younger woman and raised her empty hands. "I promise you that you have nothing to fear from me. I'll respect your boundaries and assist you any way that I can."

Jodi nodded, crying harder.

"No tea, huh? How about cocoa? I've got that."

"Sure."

She made the cocoa on the hot stove, whipping it together with a fork. She brought it to the couch with a blanket and handed both to Jodi.

"Brother Dusty-"

The name startled her for a second. She had forgotten that was the one she had given them to call her.

Jodi sniffled and wiped her nose on her sleeve. "Brother Dusty, the month since you've been gone has been so awful. One of the missionaries sent to Nevada came back. Brother Danielson. His companion died on the road, but he brought back a wife."

"Really?"

"Yeah, really. She was older, in her like late thirties I think. Brother Danielson said his companion had married them before he died. The elders argued about that, because missionaries aren't allowed to marry people. But Brother Danielson said like they had prayed about it and it was the right thing to do. And she was already pregnant anyways."

"That… might be good," she said cautiously.

"Of course it was good, but there was all this fuss about it. She wasn't a member, and she was black, and she was so much older than him. There were fights about whether the marriage was legit or if the baby would be born in covenant or not. Some of the brethren said the marriage should be annulled and she should be courted and choose someone or whatever, since she had only met two missionaries. It got freaking ugly. Brother Danielson ended up saying he'd kill anyone who tried to take his wife from him.

"But it didn't matter anyways, because she was sick. We didn't realize at first because she didn't look sick. She was just like everyone else with the fever, no temperature for a long time and then suddenly super hot. She had joined the relief society and was helping us with the children. We got her away from them as soon as we figured it out, but it was too late. Everyone who hadn't gotten sick the first time got it this time. Mikayla, Ben, and John all got it super fast. Mikayla was dead in three days but the boys held on a long time. They both died a few days ago. Patty had it before, she wasn't sick at all."

"Oh no. Not the kids. What about the women? Sister Everly and Sister Johannsen?"

"Sister Everly passed on. Sister Johannsen had it before, but she just about died taking care of the sick. But she couldn't help it much. Elder Johannsen died right in front of her. Brother Danielson and his wife died alone in their house, nobody wanted to go to them. They blamed them for bringing it back."

"So how many are left?"

"Bishop Comstock died, so Bishop Graves is in charge. There were twenty one people left when I ran away. But Bishop Graves is acting so weird."

"Weird how?"

"He said he's the prophet now. God's telling him what to do. He married Patty."

"Didn't you say she was nine?"

Jodi nodded, tearful again. "He said she's going to live in his house and learn to love him, but that he'll hold her virginity sacred for seven years."

"He's a fucking prince."

"Please don't curse at me." Jodi was still crying. "I'm just trying to tell you."

"Ok. Ok, I'm sorry. Go on."

"Sister Johannsen was remarried to Elder Sterling right away. I don't even know if she wanted to, she's been so sad since her husband died. But even then, with her as old as she is, there were fights about that, too. Every man in town wanted to marry her when her husband died. But then Bishop Graves turned on me. He said that my husband is never coming back, that God showed it to him. He said I needed to remarry, and suggested a few of the men to me. Brother Dusty, I just know Honus is alive. I would feel it if he died. I have his baby inside me, like I would know."

Dusty nodded, not committing to saying anything.

"But he kept after me. Marry this guy, marry that guy. I told him, like I am still married. But they started showing up at my house all the time, bringing me presents, offering me special things. Promising me what good husbands they would be. I didn't want to be mean to them, but it was like breaking my heart. I couldn't cheat on Honus."

"How far along are you?" Dusty looked at her belly, guessing six months at the most.

"Honus and I were married one hundred and eighty days ago, exactly. We were together for a week before he was sent out. So I'm like six months."

Dusty nodded. "So you left to get away from all that?"

Jodi started to sob again, clutching up the blanket. "No, I left when the Bishop said I would be married in a week to the man of his choosing, and that I was being stiff-necked and disobedient and I'd have to learn to submit. He issued like a proclamation that women would be given in marriage by their fathers or by the bishop from now on. Period. We don't get to decide anymore."

"I see." Dusty was boiling with an old anger, it seemed as old as the world.

"I went to his wedding with Patty. We don't have a temple, but they made do. She cried like the whole time. It was terrible. The guys all looked jealous or bored, but nobody seemed sorry for her. They were just like, 'that's how it is now.'" I tried to talk to Sister Johannsen… I guess she's Sister Sterling now… I talked to her about it. She said it's hard for Patty to understand because she's just a little girl, but that I was grown up and I should know better."

"Why didn't they wait until the baby was born? Why so soon?"

Jodi choked a little laugh and shook her head. "They don't know," she said.

"What?"

"They don't know I'm expecting. I've been wearing my sister's old clothes that are super baggy on me and tying my apron really loose. I hid when I had morning sickness and I never told anyone. I lived alone in our house, mine and Honus'. I really wanted to tell the little girls, to tell them how like awesome it was to feel him kick and whatever. But I didn't."

"Unfuckingbelievable."

"Why do you have such a potty mouth?" Jodi glared at her.

Everyone you know is dead, but let's focus on my language.

"Are you really angry at cursing at a time like this? Look, it's how people talk where I'm from. I'm sorry it offends you. I'll try to keep it under control, but this is my house."

Jodi appeared chastened. "Forgive me, Brother Dusty. I didn't mean to challenge your authority."

"Oh for fuck's… heaven's sake." Dusty stood up and took Jodi's empty cup. "You want another one?"

"Yes, thank you. Could I fix you something to eat?"

Dusty smiled, her back to the girl. "I think that's your subservient way of saying you're hungry. Am I right?" She glanced over her shoulder to see her reaction.

"No I just meant if you wanted… you don't have anybody to cook for you. I can do that. I can clean, too, and like wash clothes. I really don't want to go back. I will make myself useful and stuff if I can stay."

Dusty put the kettle back on and turned around. "Of course you can stay. What kind of heartless psycho would turn a pregnant woman out into the snow? Stay as long as you want, and I'll take care of you. I've been in labor and delivery for the last ten years. I want to ask you some questions, though."

"Sure, whatever." Jodi pulled the blanket up to her chin.

"Is this your first pregnancy?" Dusty poured out another cup of cocoa and put on two cans of soup.

"Of course it is. I told you, we just got married."

"Of course. And you said 'he.' How do you know the baby's sex?"

"I just have a feeling."

"So you didn't tell Dr. Beaumont you were pregnant, either."

"No. I was afraid to."

"Have you been taking prenatal vitamins or anything like that?"

"Yeah, I knew that was important. I took them from bishop's storehouse, but nobody noticed. They're in my coat."

"Smart girl. Any bleeding or cramping?"

"No, huh uh, not at all."

When the soup was steaming, she poured it into deep mugs and brought one to Jodi with her cocoa. She returned with her own and sat back down.

"Jodi, have you seen any babies born since the plague came through the first time?"

"No." She set her mouth in a little pink purse. She knew what was coming, but her mind was already made up.

"But you heard about it? You know that a lot of babies are born sick and they… they don't make it. You heard that, right? I'm not trying to scare you. I just want you to understand the risks of the situation."

"That doesn't matter," she said firmly.

"Why is that?"

"Because there's a new covenant. The prophet said so. Babies born into the new world and the new covenant will live."

"Is that the same prophet who just married a nine year old girl?"

"No, like the real prophet in Salt Lake City." Jodi looked like she was trying to explain something simple to someone very stupid. "He told all the bishops in his last message before we lost contact or whatever. Our babies are safe."

How convenient.

"Ok. I will do the best I can for you and your child. I'll help you any way I can. But I can't do that unless you're honest with me. Can you promise to tell me how you're feeling and if anything changes?"

Jodi nodded.

"Alright. There's a bedroom at the end of the hall that I think belonged to a teenage girl. It has its own small fireplace. I can start a fire in there, if you want to take it."

"That'd be fine."

* * * * *

Told her to be honest with me, but I'm not even trying to be honest with her. Let her figure it out or tell her? How weirded out is she going to be? Be better that she know I'm not going to try to fuck her, that I can examine her without her freaking out about it. She finds out on her own = might not be able to trust me afterward. Could take this fucking binder off. = = = = Have to tell her.

* * * * *

In the morning, Dusty had hardly slept. She had been nocturnal for too long. She got up anyway, relieved to have somebody to talk to. She found Jodi already at work.

"I was gonna surprise you with breakfast." She was in the pantry, looking at the shelves. "I can make eggs and biscuits, I think. There's some canned sausage gravy. How does that sound?"

Dusty had avoided the powdered eggs so far. She knew one day they'd have to get eaten. It wasn't a good time to be picky. "Sounds good. I'm going to make some coffee. It's instant and the creamer is dried, but it's not bad. You're not supposed to have a lot, but I could make you a weak cup."

Jodi didn't look back at her, she was reaching for the powdered eggs. "No tea, no coffee. I told you."

"Oh, right. Mormons."

"Yeah. Like I've never even had coffee. Everybody says the smell is nice but the taste is super yucky."

"You get used to it," Dusty said as she put the kettle on.

The kitchen was large but the Franklin stove was small. In the end, Dusty let Jodi shoo her out to the table so she had enough room to cook.

"So did you get a job after high school?"

"Nah, me and Honus got engaged right at my graduation. It was super romantic. I waited for him while he served his mission in Canada, I wrote him letters like every week. That was super hard. I can't believe I have to wait for him again. Anyways, he got into BYU and we were gonna move to Provo together."

"Did you apply to college, too?"

"Nah, I knew we would have kids right away. I've always wanted to be a mom. Did you ever get married?"

"No." When the kettle whistled, Dusty got up and made a cup of coffee with cream.

"Aw, that's so sad."

"It would have been sadder to have been married and have it fall apart." She sat down and stirred her coffee.

"So you were like a doctor?"

Dusty tried to remember what she had told them in Huntsville. She didn't recall, but she didn't think Jodi remembered anyway. "I was a registered nurse and midwife. I got my degree at UCSF and worked in the university hospital. Babies born every day. Always plenty of work to do."

"Wow, that's so cool." She sounded distracted.

"It was cool. I loved my job." Dusty hadn't tried at all this morning to sound like a man. She was still wearing the binder, going slowly. She waited.

After a few minutes, Jodi came out carrying two plates. "The biscuits burned on the bottom. I've never cooked them that way before. I just cut the bottoms off."

"I'm sure they'll be fine."

Jodi sat down, pushing her chair back to make room for her belly. "I swear I'm bigger every day. Are you gonna…?"

"What?" Dusty already had half a biscuit in her mouth.

"Are you gonna say a blessing, Brother Dusty?"

"Oh. Why don't you go ahead?"

Jodi smiled indulgently at her. "Dear most gracious Heavenly Father…"

Dusty chewed and swallowed unhurriedly. Jodi's prayer was almost the exact same as the ones she had heard given in Huntsville. Same words, same cadence, same sequence. Dusty waited.

"Amen." Jodi ate as though she were hungry. "I should make some fruit and veggies with lunch. I know the little guy needs them."

Dusty nodded approvingly, still mashing biscuit crumbs and sausage gravy together to cover the texture of powdered eggs. "That's a good idea, good that you're paying attention. What would you like to do today?"

"I dunno," Jodi said. "You know what I miss?"

Dusty smiled and popped her chin to encourage the answer. She was happy in the anticipation of being able to miss the lost world together. They could share it.

Like with Roxanne.

"I super miss TV."

Not at all like Roxanne. She's just a kid.

Dusty tried not to look let down. "Oh yeah? Like what?"

"I miss 'Real Housewives,' and 'The Bachelor.' They always went on the best dates. It was so romantic." She looked wistful, like she was remembering old friends.

"Oh. I don't think I ever saw either one of those."

Jodi rewarded her with nearly an hour of exposition of where the season had ended with the bachelor, who was there for the 'right reasons,' and who was pushing the envelope sexually. Dusty was bored with the subject in minutes, but she tried to take comfort in the sound of Jodi's voice. She had desperately wanted someone to talk to. She couldn't be picky about her company now.

When she had finished her breathless recap, Jodi turned to Dusty. "So, what have you been doing here alone all this time?"

"Well, I read every book on the block. They're in the dining room on the sideboard, if you want to try one."

"Nah, I don't really like to read."

There's a shock.

Jodi had washed the dishes and wiped down the kitchen. She stoked the fire and then turned around, looking for something to do.

"What'd you do in your spare time in Huntsville?"

"Canning and sewing and stuff. Like taking care of everyone, making food and fixing socks and stuff."

"What do you like to do, though?"

Jodi looked blank.

"Don't get much time off, do you?"

"I dunno. I liked to talk with the other sisters. Gossip, really. I know we're not supposed to, but it always happens. I guess there's nothing to gossip about with just the two of us here."

"Well, there might be…"

Jodi looked at her askance. "What do you mean?"

"There isn't any easy way to say this," she began.

"Oh no." Jodi looked stricken. "Please. Please don't."

"What? Why are you so scared of me?" Dusty took a step toward her, then thought better of it and stopped.

"I don't know, but I can tell you're trying to tell me something important. Is it bad news? I can't take any more bad news." She was blinking back tears.

Dusty sighed, exasperated. "It's not bad news. It's just something I want to get off my chest. It doesn't change anything."

"Ok. What?"

"I'm not a man."

Jodi stared at her.

"I've been dressing like a man since I left San Francisco. I've been much safer this way. It's not safe out there for anyone, but especially not for women."

"You're lying." Jodi looked very confused.

"What, do you want me to show you? Look at me! No beard. No Adam's apple. It's a simple disguise."

"But your figure…?"

"I'm wearing a binding vest."

"A what?"

"It's a vest that smashes your breasts down. So you can look like a guy." She itched to take it off, and this was taking longer than she expected. She had thought Jodi would see it right away and laugh a little at having been fooled for this long.

"Why would that even exist? Who would want that?"

Dusty snorted. "Lots of people you've never met. Look, why would I lie about this?"

"To get me to drop my guard so you can like take advantage of me."

Dusty rolled her eyes. "This is stupid."

She started unbuttoning the plaid shirt she was wearing. Jodi started to look away, but when the top of the vest became visible she was transfixed. The garment was very worn, and yellowed at the armpits. The front closed in a long series of tiny bra hooks. It didn't fit well or snugly anymore; Dusty had lost too much weight and it had just been worn too long. Still, it was doing a fair job of smoothing out her curves. The material had a translucent white mesh and the pink of her nipples showed through just slightly. She pushed the hooks together and started to open the vest. She reached a deep V between her breasts and her cleavage was clear.

"Ok, stop. I get it. You really aren't a man."

"Nope. I'm gonna get this thing off." She walked out of the room to go change. She pulled a sports bra out of the bottom of her pack and put it back on, followed by her shirt.

She walked back out, buttoning up. "Sorry about that. I just had to prove it to you." She looked up, but she didn't see Jodi anywhere.

"What the fuck?"

She walked around the house, looking for her. She was about to call out when she heard the snowmobile outside. She crossed to the window and looked. It was pulling up out front.

Shit shit shitty shitstorming fuck. Perfect.

She ripped her heavy winter coat off the hook by the door and put it on. Then she ran into the kitchen, picked up the wet clothes Jodi had hung up to dry and stuffed them into the oven. She turned around, looking to see if there was any other sign of the girl. She touched the gun in the back of her waistband where it always was and spotted the rifle leaning against the wall.

Safe. Everything safe. Alone here.

She went to the door. She thought about refusing to open it, but discarded the idea. Too suspicious. She looked through the peephole just as they started to knock. It was Chalmers and another man she had never seen. She opened the door.

"Hi, guys. What can I do for you? Is one of you hurt?" She did her best to deliver it with light concern, in her old Dusty low voice.

"No Brother Dusty, we're fine. This is Brother Randolph. We're looking for a member of the congregation who went missing yesterday."

"In this snow? Are you serious? That's awful." She was trying to look behind them to see if Jodi's tracks were visible in the deep snow. It had snowed all night, and there wasn't much left. She could always tell them they were her own.

"I'm afraid so. Have you seen or heard anything unusual today?" Chalmers was watching her face, his calm blue eyes boring into hers.

"Man, I wish. I haven't heard so much as a bird in days. It's pretty lonesome out here." She smiled thinly.

Chalmers nodded. "We're going to take a look around the neighborhood."

Randolph looked at him in surprise. "Shouldn't we search the house?"

Her blood pressure went up and she fought it. "You guys are welcome to come in. I've got coffee. I haven't been feeling well this week, so I've got the kettle going all the time. I'm even wearing my coat in the house." She shrugged inside her clothes as if to dig herself in deeper and pulled her neck down into the hood.

Her throwaway comment about feeling sick struck them like an arrow. Chalmers was suddenly inching his way down the porch steps.

"Oh that's fine, we don't want to bother you." He tugged at Randolph's sleeve. If you see anyone out in the snow, I'm sure you'll render aid. We'll come back and check with you in a week or so." He almost tripped in his eagerness to get away.

She waved to them from the doorway and closed up slowly. Then she threw the bolt and put her back up against the door. She heard the snowmobile start up.

"Jodi?"

The broom closet in the kitchen swung open and Jodi spilled out, trembling all over. "Thank god, oh thank god."

"They're gone. I don't know if they tracked you here or what, but they're definitely looking for you. How did you know they were coming?"

"I heard it! Didn't you hear it? That thing is super loud."

"Did you leave a note? Tell anyone where you were going?"

She shrugged. "No. People disappear sometimes. They just leave. I thought they'd like… just forget about it. You know?"

"You mean guys disappear sometimes. Have you ever lost a woman that way?"

She goggled at Dusty. "No… I didn't think of it that way."

Dusty sat down on the sofa. "Yeah, well. There's no mystery to those disappearances, anyway."

"What do you mean?"

"They're just suicides. Comstock didn't want to admit it, but it was pretty clear."

"There's no way that's true." Jodi's face set along angry lines. "Why would anybody do that?"

Dusty snorted. "Yeah, you're right. Why would they? Everything is wonderful." It came out meaner than she had meant it. She saw Jodi flinch.

Jodi got up and went to the kitchen. "I'm gonna-"

"Stay away from the windows for a while. They said they were going to search the neighborhood. I don't know if they will, but just in case."

Jodi came back into the doorway. "You're not really sick, are you?"

Dusty snorted. "No. I just told them that so they'd be too scared to come in."

Jodi stared at her, her brows coming together.

"You want to feel my head?"

Dusty expected Jodi to laugh it off, but she came straight toward her with her hand out. She laid the back of her left hand against Dusty's cheek and waited. Looking away, she cupped her palm against Dusty's forehead.

"Normal, right?"

Jodi dropped her hand. "Yeah. Yeah, just checking."

Keep checking. Please.

It was casual contact, almost clinical. But her hand was soft and small, with slender fingers. It awakened something in Dusty that she had been ignoring while it slept. Something stirred and wanted and ached. She did everything she could to coax it back to bed.

*Winter*

If that missionary brought back a live plague victim from Nevada = fever is still active in some places. Maybe she got it from a corpse?

People who never got sick, like Roxanne and most of the people in Huntsville. Immune or never exposed = the second exposure to Huntsville broke their quarantine and killed the ones who were not immune. There are those of us who got sick but fought it off, like me. Maybe no one is naturally immune and the degree of exposure determines infection. But then no one in Huntsville would have made it. Vector was cooking in the communal kitchen and they all ate together. Some people must be immune.

Those of us who got it might be able to get it again. Drilled Jodi about it a hundred times. She never had it, and she doesn't remember if anyone who died recently had previously recovered. No good with details that aren't relevant to her own interests.

Jodi has been here with me for a week. She really wants to be helpful. Very industrious, very clean. Won't waste a single bite of food and she makes her bed every morning. However, useless to talk to. Simple+childlike=dull. Has almost no imagination and anything outside of her experience she just won't believe.

Talks about television almost constantly. Wish she had watched different shows. It might be interesting to listen if she had been addicted to fiction, even if it was silly, but all she watched was reality. She repeats the plots to me, but she always leaves things out so that they don't make sense, so then I ask questions and she remembers. An incredibly tiresome pastime. Wanted company, but shit. Miss the nurses I used to work with. Mean and hard and sometimes crass, but at least they weren't dumb. Even Roxanne. Wasn't book smart, but she was cunning. Roxanne = GOT IT. Understood me without my having to explain constantly. Jodi doesn't even get jokes. Realized a few days ago I'm nice to her because we're alone here, but also because she's pretty. Just like to look at her. She's probably been treated like that her whole life. Don't like myself much when I think of that.

She finally let me examine the baby. Palpated the fundus, was able to discern length of femur.

Not receptive at all to talking about what's going to happen when the baby is born. Not interested in my experience with the plague, or in the story I got from Roxanne. Not going to scare her or torture her with the possibility, but I wish she'd at least think about it. She's going to fall apart if she doesn't prepare.

* * * * *

The snow quit one day and Dusty got bundled up to go out.

"Hey, I'm gonna skip breakfast. I'm going to walk two miles or so to the nearest neighbor that I haven't robbed yet. It will take me a couple of hours, then I'll be back. Is there anything you'd like me to look for? For you?"

She stood in the doorway tying up her scarf. Jodi came out of the kitchen looking frightened.

"You're leaving me?"

"What? No. I'm just going to walk to another house and look for supplies. I'd like some new books. Maybe find a house that has some board games? And you need some bigger clothes…"

Jodi's face was crumpling. It was all Dusty could do to hold back a sigh of exasperation and contempt.

"I'm fine. I don't need anything new." She folded her arms across her chest.

"Well I do," Dusty said simply. "And I'm going. I'll lock you in, and I doubt anyone will come looking for you today-"

"No!" She said it like she was a moment away from a tantrum; Dusty expected her to stamp her foot. "If you're leaving, then I'm going with you."

This time Dusty did sigh. She wanted some time off. Not to live alone forever, but just a short break from Jodi, filling the silence with her meaningless chatter.

Find some people, wish you were alone. Live alone, wish for people.

"You're very pregnant. You want to walk four miles in the snow?"

"You're supposed to walk when you're pregnant, right? Like for exercise? So I'll walk with you."

Dusty rolled her eyes. "In small doses, not in an endurance march. You're going to get very tired. You don't have the stamina you had before you got pregnant. This will be hard and cold and your ankles will get swollen."

Jodi shrugged. "If I'm too tired to come back, we can sleep in some other house."

"What if there's no firewood?"

She shrugged again. "Whatever. I'm bored and I don't want to stay here alone. I'm going with you."

"Fine. I can't stop you from coming with me. But I expect you to keep up. And I do not want to stay somewhere else for the night. We're taking the sled, and you do what I tell you to. Alright?"

She smiled as suddenly as she had pouted, as suddenly as she could burst into tears when she wanted. "Yay! I'll get dressed!"

"Put on a pair of sweat pants under your skirt," Dusty said, miserable by the door.

To Jodi's credit, it didn't take her long. In a scant few minutes she was back out of her bedroom, wearing sweatpants as she was told. A long skirt and a down-filled jacket went over, with a scarf and hat and a small wicker basket draped over one arm.

Dusty considered her. Jodi was a brat, but she'd been brought up in a rigid structure that only got more rigid after the plague. She would do what Dusty told her to because it was how she had always lived. At the very least, she was biddable. Dusty was grateful for that as she locked the door behind them.

They walked to the end of the yard in silence. The snow was drifted up so high that the sled skidded along on the surface at almost hip height. Dusty knew they had come to the street by the mailbox.

"So, where are we headed?"

Dusty pointed to the right. "There are two houses a couple of miles that way that I've just about cleaned out. I'd like to go the other way, I think there are more down the road a bit. The map looks like a cul-de-sac about three miles down."

"Ok."

They trudged into the street and dragged the sled slowly down the road.

"So I've been thinking about names for the baby."

Dusty looked up at the black tree branches with little white tents of snow piled on top. "Only natural. So what are your thoughts?"

"Well, if it's a boy, his middle name has to be Honus, after his father. That's an Obermeyer tradition. But I was thinking about first names. Like what about Brad? Or Ashton? Or what about Jaden? Isn't that super pretty?"

"It was really popular last year at the hospital. About every other boy was named Aiden Braden Jaden or Kaden."

Jodi was silent. Dusty didn't look, because she knew that she would be stormy.

"Then again, most of those kids are dead. So I guess it hardly matters."

Didn't mean that to sound callous. Just practical. She's pissed again. Like it's my fault.

Jodi waited a few minutes before speaking. "It might be a girl, I guess. I really feel like it's a boy, but better safe than sorry or whatever. So I was thinking about Chloe and Zoe. Or like a really super old name, like Abigail. What do you think?"

"Those are lovely," Dusty said absently.

Name plates in the neonate ward, the ones nurses slipped into the fronts of cradles. Boy Jones. Girl Rodriguez. Sometimes the parents had whole name ready to go. Dusty remembered kids named Angel and Treasure, kids named Jesus and Elvis and Belle and Martin

Luther and Kal-El. Those that weren't named after someone famous were named after someone in the family. Always some idea of who the kid should be.

"Honus and I talked about names. He really wanted to name his son George. He said that was Baby Ruth's real name."

"Babe Ruth? The baseball player?"

"Yeah. Honus and his dad are like really into sports. It's all they talk about." Jodi was grinning.

"Are you into sports too?"

"Nah, that's guy stuff. But I'm glad it makes him happy."

The road had markers to keep drivers aware of where they were on the Utah grid system. They had moved one square west of Dusty's house. It seemed like they were making good time.

In the cold air, Jodi's cheeks were pink roses and her eyes were bright. She was clearly enjoying being out of the house for a bit.

"Honus is such a sweetheart. He always surprises me with little presents. He's funny and silly. I miss him so much."

"Where was he sent again?"

"Colorado. Denver." She said it very quietly, looking at the uneven trenches her legs were cutting through the snow.

Get used to being a widow.

"Ah. Do they usually send men out who've just been married?"

"Not before. Before it was unmarried guys when they turned eighteen, and old maids who hadn't gotten married by twenty five. But Bishop Comstock said it had to be young men, and there weren't that many of those. So they let us get married and have a week together, and then sent him out. It was kind of like a blessing, because now when he comes home I'll be able to surprise him with a baby."

"Will he be happy?"

"Of course he will! He wants to be a daddy, that's why we got married."

"Is he handsome?"

"Oh my gosh yes he is so cute. He's taller than me, like way tall. He has brown hair and blue eyes and the best smile. He played basketball in high school. I was a freshman when he was a senior and I was crushing on him from day one. I used to go to his games. He was gonna play for BYU." She looked wistful and proud, as if recalling achievements of her own.

"He sounds lovely."

"Yeah, so like when he got called to Ottawa he was super excited. He really wanted to be called to like Japan or something, but whatever. So I promised I would wait and we made plans and stuff. I never thought I'd have to wait like this again."

"I never thought I'd do a lot of things I've had to do since this all started."

Jodi looked at her, a little concern wrinkling her smooth forehead. "Like what?"

Dusty waited a minute, looking up and down the white road. "I think we're about halfway."

"Can we take a break?" Jodi's voice was plaintive, not quite whining.

"We really can't," Dusty told her. "We need to get somewhere warm before we sit down. It's no good for you to be in this cold, and it would only prolong your exposure if we take a break out here. We're almost there."

"Ok." Jodi launched into another long explanation of her favorite TV show, this time the scandalous real life of a group of rich and famous sisters. Dusty checked out and just said "Yes" or "Mhmm" or "Oh really?" in the right places. She reached back and put her hand on her gun periodically, like touching a talisman.

Finally, Dusty saw the outline of a house up ahead. It was two stories tall and the front door was drifted in. The snow was at least good for showing whether people had been in and out recently.

"Look!" She pointed it out to Jodi, who snapped her head toward it.

"Oh yay! We found it!"

They ran haltingly, struggling to get through the snow in the road and to the edge of the yard. As they got closer, Dusty saw that it was a large house with a huge bay window. She smiled.

"This could be good."

The door was unlocked. Jodi opened it and they walked in together.

Dusty went straight to the decorative fireplace with a dry stack of oak beside it and looked around for kindling. She took the magazines off the coffee table and used them to start a fire. She wrenched the flue open and sat patiently, feeding the flames until it roared. She told Jodi to sit down in front of it and warm up, especially her legs.

"Try to stop me," said Jodi as she shucked off her snow-caked shoes.

Dusty stomped her feet and started to check the place out.

It was obviously a family home. Stains on the couch and pictures on the mantle. A plastic high chair at the kitchen table. A tub of toys in a cozier family room, located off the side of the main entrance. She opened up the pantry and took a look. There was soup here she thought they should take, among other things. She thought she'd let Jodi check the food, since she did most of the cooking. She went up the back staircase and started looking through the bedrooms.

The master bedroom had a dead couple in the bed, their arms laid over the smaller corpses of their children under the blankets.

Well, good for you. Sound decision.

She took a bottle of frozen shampoo from the windowsill above their shower and tucked it into her pack. None of the clothes in the large closet looked like a good fit for either of them. She closed the door and moved to the next room.

She found a handful of board games in a closet and stacked them at the top of the stairs. She loaded her bag with books, including about twenty from a young girl's bedroom. The kid had favored science fiction and fantasy and Dusty's eyes grew large at the sight of them. She thought she'd love to travel in some other worlds for a change. In a boy's room she found another stack, mostly adventures. She was so glad for this discovery that she bounced up and down on the balls of her feet at the sight of them. She thought the books alone made up for the walk.

She heard Jodi coming up the stairs. "Hey are you warmed up then? Will you take that stack of games down to the sled?"

Silence.

"Jodi?"

She came out of the bedroom and walked out into the hallway. She didn't see anyone. Her breathing got fast and ragged and she put her right hand behind her, ready to draw.

"Jodi? Damn it, Jodi, answer me."

She came close enough to see that the master bedroom door was open again, and Jodi was standing there, staring at the dead couple in the bed.

"Jodi, you scared the shit out of me. You shouldn't be in here. And don't fucking ignore me when I call you."

Jodi turned on her, suddenly furious. "How can you talk like that in here? Don't you have any respect? This was their house, and they died here, together. I hope they were sealed in the temple."

Dusty tugged at her sleeve. "Come on, Jodi. Please get out of here. You shouldn't be around dead bodies, not with the baby."

"In the celestial kingdom, they will be together forever." She nodded resolutely, but her eyes were troubled.

"Good. That is great for them. Let's please get out of here, ok?"

Jodi turned away and left the room.

"You should try the last door on the right there for clothes," Dusty said.

"I don't think we should take anything," Jodi said, turning to her.

"What?"

"This isn't ours to take. It belongs to someone."

Dusty was baffled. "They're dead. Dead people don't own anything. We're living and we need it. I don't think they'd mind, but even if they did, they're dead. One more time. Dead. Most of the people in the world, dead. We're gonna take what we need."

"Not me. My clothes are fine. I'm not taking anything."

"Jesus Christ."

"Don't take the Lord's name in vain, please." Jodi's mouth was a thin line of disapproval.

For a white hot second, Dusty wished she had continued the illusion that she was a man. She could have cowed Jodi into shutting up if she had that authority. As it was, they were going to have to wrestle it out. She took a deep breath.

"Alright. Your choice. Don't take anything. I'm going to load up and then we're out of here. We'll leave the other houses for another day."

She pushed past Jodi, picked up the games, and headed down the stairs.

"Wait!"

She turned back on the landing.

"What?"

"We should bury them."

Dusty turned her back and kept walking downstairs. "You bury them. I'll wait."

She loaded up the sled, pretending to not pay attention. She had an ear cocked, waiting to hear if Jodi actually tried to get the bodies out of the bed. She stacked up the games and threw down her backpack. She didn't hear the thumps of bodies. What she heard was Jodi vomiting.

She came down the stairs, pale and shaking, wiping her mouth.

"You good?"

"Whatever."

Jodi sat down by the fire again.

"Exactly." Dusty stalked back into the kitchen. She looked over the shelves. To herself, she muttered, "I wonder if I can make cake without fresh eggs."

"You can."

Jodi had come quietly to the kitchen door. Dusty turned around to face her.

"There's tricks. I learned how as a girl scout."

So domestic. I'd be annoyed except that I benefit from it.

"Ok. I'm gonna grab some cake mixes, then. Cake sounds good. What do you say?"

"I guess it's ok."

"Good." She grabbed three boxes of mix and tucked them under her arm.

Quietly, Jodi came into the pantry and started picking out cans. Dusty didn't say anything about her sudden reversal of morals. She didn't want to fight. She wanted to get loaded up and get back on the road.

"You warmed up enough to go back out there?"

Jodi pouted a little. "Are you sure we shouldn't just stay here?"

"It's early afternoon. We can totally make it back. Come on." She went back to the sled and stacked up the cake mixes, flat on their side. "There's lots of food here. We should remember and come back if we start to run low."

Jodi came up behind her and put her canned goods on the sled. "How long are you planning to stay in Eden?"

"I want to wait out the winter before I move on. If I'd known it snowed like this in Utah, I might have stayed somewhere else."

Jodi laughed a little. "I'm from Ogden. I haven't seen snow like this, ever. Not in my whole life. This is like the worst winter I've ever seen."

"Perfect timing, then."

"Yeah. Totally."

The fire had died down. Dusty considered shoveling the ashes out, then decided not to bother. They closed up the house and left it unlocked, then set out to return. Dusty got ahead, dragging the sled slightly behind. They kept to their earlier tracks, and Dusty thought about the trail they had left. She deliberately walked into the snow that kept their paths separate and mussed them together. She didn't want anyone to be able to tell that two had come and gone. Indeterminate tracks were better than an exact number. When she looked behind them, she saw a long churned-up track that might have been made by anything at all. She thought about laying the warm gun in the snow beside her, just for a moment, so that anyone who followed their tracks would see the impression of it. She dismissed the idea as stupid, but she felt uncomfortably exposed.

She needn't have worried. It started to snow again before they got halfway home.

Dusty looked at Jodi as the house came into view. Snowflakes lay thick on her red-gold eyelashes. One or two lit on her pink lips and melted there. She caught Dusty looking at her.

"What?"

"Nothing."

It does no good to tell a beautiful woman how beautiful she is. If she already knows, it gives her power over the fool who tells her. If she does not, there is nothing that can be said to make her believe it. Dusty did not know everything, but she knew that.

"Come on. Let's get in and build that fire."

# Chapter Seven

*Still Winter*
*Forever Winter*
*The Winter of Our Discontent*

Starting to figure out how to live with each other. Gives me space when I'm reading, and I can stand her so much better after a little time and silence. Jodi = sweet. Heats water for my bath, been able to talk her around to a few subjects of conversation that don't make me want to scream. So sheltered = So fucking dull. So glad I have new books. Good ones I haven't read.

Doesn't seem to need any time alone. Not sure she's ever had any. Not sure she has any thoughts she doesn't say.

* * * * *

They settled into a routine. Neither of them set terms. They did not negotiate or ever directly address what they needed from one another, but the days fell into a rhythm.

Dusty got up first thing in the mornings and saw to the fire. She banked the coals, scuttled the ashes, brought a stack of wood within reach and got it roaring again. By the time she came to Jodi's room to do the same, Jodi was up. The younger woman always cooked, Dusty had given up even trying. Jodi was a dab hand with what they had, never wasting and always making something filling and edible. When Jodi wasn't cooking, she cleaned house, washed and mended their clothes and reliving television shows that she missed terribly. Dusty tried to draw her out on reminiscences of Honus, but Jodi grew silent on that topic.

Jodi's belly grew rounder and bigger every day, hard as a pumpkin. The two of them could share the occasional moment of joy when she would suddenly light up and wave for Dusty to lay hands on her wide, taut belly. She would never speak at these times, as if the baby were a fish that might be frightened away. She would wave, eyes wide, mouth closed. Dusty never grew tired of this, never passed up the chance. The child was alive, kicking like a soccer player, long-limbed and whole.

Now in the seventh month of pregnancy, Jodi was doing well. Dusty watched her carefully. Her appetite had increased. She got plenty of sleep. She was active and in fine spirits every day. She went out into the snow to relieve herself with regularity. Dusty could tell the baby had not yet turned. He was still head-up and face-forward. She considered turning him but she thought it could wait. Dusty did not want to hope. She tried to keep hope out of her, shutting all the doors and locking them with the keys of reason and evidence and precedent. Still, she could feel it seeping in, incorporeal and deathless, refusing to be refused.

In the evenings, Jodi would make dinner. She could indeed make cake without fresh eggs or butter or milk, and the results weren't bad. Dusty would prod her for some kind of conversation beyond the immediate. Sometimes her efforts were rewarded. Even reminiscences from Jodi's Norman Rockwell childhood could be interesting on occasion. Dusty tried telling her own stories, but she knew that Jodi was immediately bored. They felt how keenly different they were and tried to glide over it. Dusty ended every evening by reading a book in a wingback chair in the living room. She had tried to read aloud for Jodi a few times, but Jodi would fall asleep or ask wildly off-topic questions. Dusty stopped trying. There was much they could not share. They shared Jodi's pregnancy.

Dusty woke in the middle of the night with her heart pounding. She thought it was only another nightmare. She had them less frequently with Jodi in the house, but they still happened. She was trying to get her heart rate back down when the sound that had awakened her returned.

Snowmobile.

It was running at top speed, the engine whining and echoing off every tree and still surface in the silent night. She bolted out of bed in the flannel long underwear she had been wearing and pulled the pistol off her bedside table. She put it in her waistband without thinking and it slid down her ass and into the leg of her pajamas. Cursing, she kicked it out on to the floor and picked it up again. She carried it into Jodi's bedroom. She shook the girl awake.

"What?"

"Shhh! Listen."

Dusty jerked her head toward the sound, but Jodi's eyes were already huge with terror.

"Can you get under the bed?"

She shook her head. "I'm too big. No way. The closet?"

Dusty nodded to her and she slid off the bed and hastily began to make it. "Good idea," Dusty said.

She padded down the stairs and picked up the rifle that she had leaned against the door. She held both guns and sank to the floor beside the front window. She was calm. She brought the rifle up to rest it on the windowsill and pointed it out into the darkness. She hadn't lit a candle, she had the embers of the fire. No stars, no moon. The vague blurry impression of snow falling.

A black shape came pounding up the porch, not sneaking, very fast. Fists banged the door.

Dusty leapt to her feet and backed up, setting the rifle down. She held the revolver at arm's length.

"Fuck off!" She bellowed it at the door.

"Jodi! Jodi! I'm looking for my wife, Jodi Obermeyer!"

Upstairs, she heard the commotion of Jodi bursting out of the closet. She came down the stairs in her nightgown, taking the stairs so fast that Dusty held her breath. She stepped back and Jodi flew straight to the door, screeching.

"Honus? Honus, baby? Oh my god, Honus!" She flung open the door. The cold wind ripped her nightgown back and outlined her breasts and belly in the firelight. Her loose red-gold hair streamed back and she slit her eyes against it, shielding her face with her hand.

"Is it really you?"

A tall figure with broad shoulders walked through the door. He pulled off a ski mask and revealed a handsome bearded face. His hair was dark and his cheeks were hollow. His eyes glistened in the low light and he wrapped his arms around Jodi and sobbed openly.

"Thank god, oh thank god."

They stood that way, crying on one another, for several minutes. Dusty had lowered the gun and shut the door. She waited quietly. She knew she'd eventually be remembered.

Honus sank to his knees and held Jodi's belly, kissing it over and over. "My baby, oh my baby. I didn't know, but I prayed. I hoped."

Jodi stroked his hair with both hands, smiling through tears. "I knew you'd come home. I knew it in my heart. Oh, Honus."

He turned his head to listen to the child within the womb and his eyes met Dusty's. He stood up slowly.

"You must be Brother Dusty. I can't thank you enough for taking care of my wife…" He started to offer his hand.

"She's not Brother anybody. She's just Dusty. She pretended to be a man in Huntsville. Tell him, Dusty."

"It's true. Just Dusty."

Honus looked her over, top to bottom. She saw a mixture of confusion and disbelief cross his face. She thought she saw a little disgust, as well.

"You're really… so you're pretending…?"

"I'm safer as a man." Dusty crossed her arms and waited.

Damned if I need to explain myself to you. Be glad I'm not fucking your wife. Asshole.

Honus' face relaxed. He looked relieved as if he had been able to hear her thoughts and knew himself a lucky man.

"Let me shake your hand anyway, since I surely do thank you. I'm so glad she's safe and the baby is safe and I found them. Thank you so much."

Dusty uncrossed her arms and shook, still adjusting to his presence.

"Honus, sit down. You look starved. Let me fix you something-"

"No, you two sit, I'll make something. I'm sure you want to be close to him right now…" Dusty started for the kitchen, then thought better of it.

"Are you alone?" She looked toward the door again.

Honus nodded. "My companion died in Colorado. I returned alone. I didn't even tell Bishop Sterling I was taking off."

"Anyone from Huntsville following you? Did you steal that snowmobile?"

"No, I came home on it. Nobody is plowing, it's all snow from here to there. Thank god for the snowmobile. I didn't tell anyone about your note."

"Bishop Sterling?" Jodi looked confused.

"What note?" Dusty was more interested in how he had found them.

"Bishop Comstock died and left Bishop Graves in charge. I

guess he had an accident or something a while back and now Bishop Sterling has the mantle. You know there's hardly anyone left?" He reached into the inside pocket of his jacket and pulled out a sheet of vellum.

Jodi turned to Dusty. "We always said that if something happened and one of us had to leave, our secret note place was in our wedding album. There's an envelope in there, like glued to the page, with an invitation that my mom made. There's blank vellum in there for a note, so I left one for Honus when he got back." She turned her eyes adoringly back to Honus' face. She had pronounced vellum vell-oom, as if she had never said it out loud before.

"I was crazy at first when they told me you had taken off, out into the snow. They said you were acting weird and disobedient and trying to… well, showing interest in other men. And you just took off one night without telling anyone. So I sat alone in our house, thinking that couldn't have been true. I pulled out our pictures and started looking, and then it hit me. I was only home for maybe five or six hours. I just went to the bishop and told him I was going to find you, dead or alive. And then I took off for this place, as fast as I could."

They beamed at each other. Dusty was satisfied. She got up and went to the kitchen. She pulled together a meal of hoecakes with fake bacon bits and some herb gravy. She cooked the cake on the stovetop, listening to the conversation in the other room.

"You took that snowmobile all the way home?"

"Dragging a sled of gasoline. I sure did."

"What happened to Elder Langdon?"

"I don't want to talk about it, sweetheart. Not just yet. Ok?"

"Ok. Yeah, ok. Did you actually make it to Denver?"

"We… did. We did. I don't really want to talk about that either. Denver. Not yet."

"Well, what took you so long? You were supposed to be back months ago!" Jodi's voice was nearing the whining point. Dusty knew she was near tears.

"I'm so sorry, honey. Terrible things happened along the way. All I could think about was getting home to you. I am so blessed to find you here, with our baby. So blessed. I can't believe I got this far."

Dusty brought out the hoecakes with a side of warmed green beans. She presented it to him and he disentangled himself from Jodi's arms to accept the food. "Thank you, Sister-"

"Just Dusty, please. Eat, you look starved."

Honus laid the plate reverently in his lap and folded his arms. Jodi folded hers as well. Dusty watched, waiting.

"Dear Heavenly Father, thank you so much." Honus burst into tears. He struggled to get a hold of himself. "You know what's in my heart. I am so grateful at this moment, for everything, for every breath. Thank you. Amen."

He tore into the food like he hadn't eaten well in weeks. Looking at the sunken parts of his face, the prominent bones in his hands, Dusty thought maybe he hadn't.

"Drink plenty, go slow. Your body will get used to it."

He drank, blinking.

They sat with him in silence while they ate. Jodi stared at him, her eyes shining with happiness and the deep satisfaction of having been proved right. Dusty found it impossible to look at anything but the fire. It was too intimate, too odd, and she found herself deeply uncomfortable being three where once were two. He didn't want to talk about where he had been and so there wasn't anything to talk about.

Dusty took his dishes to the kitchen and washed them. Jodi led Honus to the back of the house where the bedrooms were located, three along a line with a bathroom at the end. She could hear them whispering on the other side and waited for the sound of a closing door. She followed them after a minute, hoping suddenly that she didn't have to hear them fucking before she fell asleep. She hoped it with an emotion that she couldn't identify.

She reached her bedroom door and stopped. Jodi had gone into the bedroom she had claimed, the one that had previously belonged to a teenage girl in the before time. Dusty's bedroom stood open, the bed was made and a candle had been lit for her. The third bedroom door was closed. Neither of them had used this one; the bed sagged in the middle and they thought it had belonged to an older family member because of its fussy quality. Dusty put her ear to the door and heard Honus moving around in there, probably undressing for bed. She jerked away from it and looked back to Jodi's room. She was in there, humming. Dusty looked back and forth between the two, puzzled.

Jodi was ecstatic to see him. Why didn't she take him to bed with her?

Mystified, Dusty went to bed.

* * * * *

The rhythm of days started to reassert itself. Honus took more than his share of chores and offered to go out raiding on his own. Jodi resisted this at first, afraid to let him out of her sight. He won her over with his first trip, taking the snowmobile and returning in less than half the time a walk would have taken, bringing with him extra gasoline, candles, and cans of chocolate syrup. He was excited to observe Jodi's check-ups and delighted in feeling the baby move and kick. Their joy in anticipation was amplified when they came together, and Dusty couldn't imagine trying to tell them not to get their hopes up.

She started to think of reasons why their baby might make it. The Huntsville ward had been isolated from the disease, and maybe Jodi had never really been exposed. Maybe the constant cold made it difficult for the virus to multiply or move. Maybe the two of them were both naturally immune and could pass on that immunity. She felt like a medieval doctor, working without germ theory or any understanding of immunity. She was reasoning about this disease with hardly any understanding of its virulence or nature. Hope was with her; it would not go away.

They did the same for themselves and each other, but their

frame of reference was not epidemiology.

"But if the original covenant was damaged, and we're married in the restored covenant, then the baby should be fine."

"That is what the prophet said. But none of the sisters in Huntsville showed any sign while I was there." Jodi's thin, fine eyebrows rushed together.

Honus couldn't stop smiling. "I know. But they're older, and they might not have been… very intimate all the time."

Jodi blushed.

Kill me.

"Anyway, we did everything right. We waited until we were married, we were joined together by the bishop, our baby will be born in covenant. We're not sinless, but we're faithful and obedient. This can't go on forever. Healthy adults can have healthy babies. We might be among the first, but we won't be the last." He nodded to himself, satisfied. Sure.

They wove this narrative of surety to themselves every time either one of them felt doubt. They returned to it over and over. Their faith was the touchstone and they checked again and again to ensure that their gold was the real thing. Dusty was always quiet during this exchange, never sure what to say. Their jargon was thick.

Dusty was grateful to have someone new to talk to. It felt terrible to admit it, but she was tired of Jodi. Honus was smarter than his wife. He was funny and even quick sometimes, and could see the solution to a problem steps ahead of Jodi and only a few behind Dusty. He was terribly interested in how Jodi had come to Utah and she told the story again, but kept a few things back.

When she came to the end of it she asked, "So what happened in Colorado?"

Honus looked down at his straight razor where it lay against the strop in his lap. "I don't… I'm not sure I can tell you."

"Why not?"

"I… we saw some terrible things. And I lost my companion. I came back without him. I just… I don't know what would be gained by telling it. It would only upset Jodi."

Jodi was napping in her bedroom.

"So just tell me. I won't repeat it to her. I'm very curious, though. I know conditions are rough out there. You know what I went through-"

"It wasn't like that!" His cheeks colored and she could see his pulse throbbing in his long, thin neck. "It was like… Heart of Darkness. It was like being on another planet. I can't even describe it."

"Do you keep a diary?"

He looked up at her. "Why would you ask me that?"

She shrugged. "I do. I always have, but lately it's felt even more important. I'm processing all this, the changes in the world, everything. It's like a mental health exercise."

Honus sighed. "Did you know missionaries are required to keep a diary?"

"No, I didn't. So did you keep one?"

"I did. It's in the saddlebags on the snowmobile. I don't ever want my son to read it. Every night I think of burning it."

Quick, without a thought. "Give it to me."

"What?"

She was thinking fast, knowing she had to bring him over to the idea before he had a chance to think twice. "It's the story of a missionary working in a field that no one has ever faced. It should be kept for… for whoever is left to read it."

I'm greedy for it. I want the intimacy of someone's whole thoughts. I want to get past his gatekeeper.

He didn't speak for a second. "I can't. I just can't. I'm too ashamed of it. I'm sorry." He picked up the blade and the strop. He walked back into his room and shut the door.

She sat motionless for a long time. When she thought it had been long enough, she crept to the door.

Turning the latch with agonizing slowness, she opened the door as silently as she could. Cold wind blasted her in the face. She put one of Honus' shoes in front of the door to hold it open and keep it from swinging against the wall if the wind suddenly gusted.

Glancing back over her shoulder, she picked her way down to the snowmobile. The wind cut through her clothes; she hadn't stopped to bundle up. With freezing hands, she pulled open Honus' saddlebags. She pawed through pairs of jeans and a stack of juice boxes. Tucked against the side of the leather, she found one slim linen-covered journal. It was tied shut with a ribbon. Hastily, she closed the bag and dashed back toward the warm yellow glow of the open door.

Closing the door as slowly and quietly as she had opened it, she held her prize at her thigh, ready to hide it if necessary. Sitting down with it, she pulled at the knot in the ribbon. It yielded softly and the deed was done. She held Honus' diary in her hands, and she could not have stopped herself if she tried.

## THE BOOK OF HONUS OBERMEYER AS SCRIBED BY THE UNNAMED MIDWIFE

*Middle of the night, middle of the winter*

Shouldn't be doing this, but I have to know. Skipped most of the early travel. They walked and rode bikes for a long time through Utah, they didn't see anybody. What I wanted to get down was this story. Starts about a month in.

*Day 34*

Elder Langdon and I arrived in Grand Junction late last night. As we were advised, we are trying to find the temple in Denver but I doubt if we will ever reach that place. The desolation of the road that brought us here is very discouraging. We try to keep fear at bay, to derive strength from the Lord, but our hearts are heavy.

We have seen no live persons. The dead lay in every building, in parked cars, just everywhere. Some of them killed themselves or each other, wasting the gift of life given to them by Heavenly Father. Even in times of such trial, it's still a gift. I've stopped crying. But I am troubled. I fervently hope that Colorado holds more promise than we found in Utah outside of Huntsville. I pray that we find people to bring home with us to enrich our ward.

*Day 35*

We found the stake center here in Grand Junction, but it's utterly deserted. We fed ourselves from the storehouse and spent the night in the chapel. It is bitterly cold here, especially at night. We studied scriptures by candlelight and Elder Langdon led us in a song. He hasn't spoken to me much in the last few days, and this is turning into a very lonely mission. He woke in the middle of the night crying. I hadn't fallen asleep. When I asked him what was wrong, he said he missed his mother.

I miss mine, too.

*Day 37*

Staying in a ruined Wal-Mart tonight, somewhere along the highway. We saw the sign and Elder Langdon just headed for it without even a word. I knew it would be emptied inside and I was right. It must have been the first place people looked.

It was like a war zone inside. What hadn't been looted was destroyed. Some sections were cleaned out. There were no bikes, no camping equipment, and no knives. Only the most impractical shoes were left. The grocery section smelled like rot and we had to content ourselves with cookies and crackers. Elder Langdon did not want to read scriptures or talk at all tonight. He slept on a pallet of dog food. When I knew he was asleep, I prayed for him.

*Day 40*

I don't know how to talk to Elder Langdon about his indiscretion. I'm embarrassed to bring it up. It's not like I've never done it. It's much harder now that I'm married and I know what the blessings of the covenant are like. I'm tempted every day, but it's for her sake that I keep myself pure. I guess he doesn't have anyone to feel that way about, and he's still a virgin. I feel pity for him. Maybe if I can approach it in sympathy rather than in judgment, he'll understand.

*Day 41*

I guess all our conversation did was convince him to go away when he does it. At least he'll stop waking me up.

*Day 42*

I'm certain that we're lost. We left the main highway when we ran into an accident that blocked up the road, but now we can't find it. We're using his AAA map and I see where it should be, but I can't seem to get us back there. Heavenly Father, I feel like a failure. Please send us someone to talk to, someone to minister to. Please give our days and our work meaning. Please help Elder Langdon to make his heart contrite and seek you again. He feels very far away from me today.

*Day 43*

I miss Jodi so much. I remember the first day I met her. She was so pretty in her Halloween costume. I think she was a princess. We danced together and Sister Eggers said to leave room between us for a quad. We laughed but we did it. I can't stop thinking of her smile, her soft skin. I was married to her for only a week before Heavenly Father and the bishop sent me away. I don't want to be bitter toward Him or my missionary work, but I feel cheated. I should be with her now. I asked Elder Langdon if he had ever been in love. He looked at me and burst out laughing, I laughed too, but then he started sobbing. I guess it was the wrong thing to ask. Probably he was, with some girl who died. I apologized, but that didn't fix it. Of course.

*Day 47*

We are both sure someone is following us.

We keep hearing weird noises in the middle of the night. We're somewhere near Glenwood Springs, and we saw smoke from fires coming down the hill. We got excited that there might be people here, but we didn't see anyone. We walked all day, trying to listen for the sounds of life anywhere, or smell smoke. After that first sign, we saw nothing. But then, at night, we heard the sound of someone playing the guitar. I'm sure of it. It worked its way into my dream, and I was dreaming about that fireside I went to when Brice Stewart was playing for us. But then I remembered that Brice was dead and I woke up, but whoever it was kept playing. I got up but Langdon was still asleep. I went outside and heard it clearer. The guitar was far away, playing the intro to a Led Zepplin song I can't remember the name of. I called out into the darkness and the playing stopped. I called out again, but nobody answered. I waited, and I'm sure I heard it. I'm sure. I stood there for a minute, not believing.

It was a girl. She was laughing.

I went back inside and woke up Elder Langdon. He was cranky and told me it was just a dream. It wasn't. I laid back down and listened hard, but I didn't hear anything else.

I was pretty sore in the morning and I didn't want to talk about it if he didn't believe me. He barely said anything. We read scriptures in silence and ate canned beans and spam. At night, he conked right out, but I stayed up. A few hours after nightfall, it started.

"Yoo-hoo!"

I watched Langdon's eyes snap wide open. He heard it that time.

"Yoooooooo-hooooo! Boys! Pretty boys! Come out and play!"

I started to get up, but Langdon grabbed my arm to hold me back. "What if it's a trap?"

he asked me.

"It's a girl," I told him. "Can't you tell it's a girl?"

"Maybe it's just someone pretending."

That high voice came again from outside, floating in the still, cold air. "I wish I had some pretty boys to keep me company. I wish I could see those pretty boooooooys."

There was something about the way she called us that was like a bully taunting. Or like a farmer calling pigs. The hair on my arms stood up and I know it was a prompting of the spirit to keep away, but I couldn't help it.

I went back outside and yelled back. "Is someone there?"

More laughter. "Nope, nobody is here."

I tried calling out again, but she was gone. I think her voice was coming from above us somehow, but I don't know how that's possible. In the morning we looked for tracks or signs. We didn't find anything.

At least Langdon believed me now. The next day we hatched a plan to make it look like we had gone to bed, but actually we were going to be up on the roof, under covers, and figure out who was out there. I was freaked out, but Langdon was excited.

"Why wouldn't she just come talk to us?"

He shrugged. "She doesn't know us. Maybe she's all alone and afraid."

"Then why wouldn't she just hide?"

"I don't know. Maybe she's lonely and she really does want to meet us, but she's making sure we're not crazy first."

I couldn't make sense of it. But we are going to try hiding out on the roof. Maybe that will work.

*Day 49*

Didn't hear anything last night. Maybe tonight she'll be back. Langdon said he thought it was because it was cloudy last night so maybe she stayed in, in case of rain. I think

* * * * *

Cuts off here. Nothing until two pages past. Getting tired, going to stop here. Creepy. Also don't want to get caught. Or I do. I want to talk to him about this.

No, don't get caught.

# Chapter Eight

The story of Duke and Roxanne was never written. The night the midwife started reading Honus' missionary diary, Duke and Roxanne were riding fast down an open expanse of the I-5 just north of Los Angeles. They had climbed the pass and were enjoying the easy feel of the long glide downhill. Roxanne had let her hair grow out and had tied a red bandana in a kerchief to keep it out of her eyes. Duke wore a balaclava to keep his beard from whipping his face but he never knew his hair hit Roxanne as she rode behind. She never brought it up.

They had taken their time moving down the inland of California. The abandoned farms on either side of the road supplied fruits and nuts. They stopped and raided the small roadside outfits. They slept in their tent until it started to get cold, then switched to a series of motel rooms along the highway. They talked long into the night, almost every night. Duke told the kind of stories gathered from a life on the road. Roxanne told stories from a life in casinos. They could make each other laugh. They were a match of convenience, but a good match still.

They talked each other through the plague again and again. Roxanne suggested they hunt for newspapers while they raided, but they never found any. They started fires with gossip and fashion magazines. Roxanne looked at the faces of the women in the flames and wondered if any of them made it.

Duke, for his part, tried to play the hero. He was a good hunter and a good shot. He told Roxanne over and over that he would kill, that he would do anything to protect her. She knew that he was telling the truth, his conviction was all over him. She also knew that there might be nothing he could do, and she accepted that.

He taught her to use the Magnum. It was too big for her, and she was never ready for the kick. But she could aim it, and she could shoot it. When they rode, she wore it. When they walked, he did.

The radio on the bike worked. When they were in hills and canyons, they lost track of the broadcast about Costa Rica. Sometimes the broadcast quit for days. The loop changed. The Spanish version disappeared, and the voice of the announcer was different. One day the voice had said Nicaragua instead of Costa Rica. Duke and Roxanne weren't sure what it meant, but they hadn't seen anyone in a long time. They moved toward any sign of humanity they could find.

All around them lay the ruins of the Central Valley. The farming basin of California had depended upon water from other states brought in by electric power. When the power shut off, the valley had dried up quickly, precipitously. More than a few people had died when the bottled water ran out. They had climbed into cars and on to bikes, and they had given in and drank roadside farm runoff water, soaked in pesticides and fertilizer. In some cities, people died of mayhem and mishap. People who could not live without constant care ran out of medicine, ran out of luck, ran out of time. Public works failed and disaster followed but no disaster is faster, more assured, or crueler than a lack of water. Of the fraction that were left, thousands died of thirst.

The night that Honus' diary lost its privacy, Duke and Roxanne had stayed up late in order to make it into LA. They thought that on the outskirts of the city, their odds of foraging would be better and their accommodations might be nicer.

Roxanne had to shout into Duke's ear for him to hear as they rode, but she talked to him sometimes anyway.

"I hope we can find an empty room. That last place looked like the plague had hit during a convention or something."

He nodded and slowed down to take the first exit on the north end of Los Angeles. As he expected, the exit and the roads around it were choked with cars. He putted slowly through, the sound of the motorcycle chopping the night. He pulled into a gas station and began the tiresome process of hunting for and prying open the hatch. He was kneeling on the ground with his tubing and gas can out when the shot went off.

Roxanne was surprised, but sprang from where she leaned against the bike and drew her gun. Duke looked up but did not move.

They seemed to come from everywhere. All of them were men. Some wore uniforms or pieces of uniforms that had once identified them as National Guard, LAPD, and FEMA. The rest were in street clothes but almost all had the opaque and rigid bearing of military men. The one who had fired wore military garb. He pulled back his pistol and holstered it again. He stepped forward and addressed Duke.

"The gasoline in this station is property of the military garrison of Los Angeles, under the command of General Hertz. I'm placing you under arrest for stealing."

Duke rose slowly, his hands out. "Look, I didn't know. We can just go. I'm sorry."

"I'm afraid that won't work." A tall Mexican man in an LAPD uniform in good condition stepped forward. "The theft has already taken place, you'll have to appear before the general."

Roxanne didn't speak. She watched. Nearly every man spread out around the gas station was staring at her, except for the ones who were speaking to Duke. Guys in charge, she thought. She was right.

Military man was a short, square, career sort. He wore chevrons on his shoulders and mirrored sunglasses over his eyes, even at night. "Those are the rules."

Duke looked at Roxanne. She did not look back. She watched the army they faced.

Chevrons finally looked at her, seeming to follow Duke's gaze as if he hadn't noticed her before. "Ma'am. We have a female barracks back at our base. We'd be happy to put you up there while your man here stands trial."

Roxanne drilled him hard with her eyes. She couldn't see past his asshole glasses, but she was pretty sure he was lying.

She looked back and forth between him and the cop, deciding.

Eventually, she turned her eyes back to the glasses, seeing only her own blazing black ghost in the diffuse light.

"If you let him go without hurting him, I'll go back with you."

Chevrons flinched. The cop next to him shifted uneasily and the ripple went through the ranks. She could hear some whispering and a few low laughs.

"Now what makes you think that's how we do things? We're just trying to keep law and order, ma'am."

Roxanne lifted her chin a little. "So, since I didn't steal any gas, I'll just be on my way then. You can take Duke to the general alone."

He grinned beneath his glasses and she saw his sadism in it.

"Well I don't know about that."

"Accomplice," muttered the cop negligently, looking away. "You'll have to come in for questioning, too."

She tried the cop this time. "How many women in your "female barracks?" One? Two maybe?"

One of the ones in a FEMA suit came forward. "No, ma'am. Lots of women survived the fever with proper care. There are thousands of women alive in LA, and about a hundred live in our barracks."

Roxanne watched the crowd. That was a lie, too. She wasn't sure by how much, but it wasn't right.

"That's great! Where I was in Vegas there were hardly any girls at all who came through. My best friend even got sick." She spoke up loud, so the crowd could hear her. "I bet a lot of you fellows saw your wives and girlfriends though the fever too, right? Daughters? Mothers? Wasn't that fever a bitch, though?"

A few of them looked away.

The cop came forward, pulling the cuffs off his belt. He came to Duke's elbow.

"Sir, you're under arrest for stealing from the garrison. You and your female are ordered to come in for questioning."

He snicked one cuff around Duke's wrist, then the other. Duke had been arrested before. He looked around and knew himself outnumbered. He thought if he went along, the two of them might come through this. He trusted. He did not resist.

Roxanne felt her heart in her eyes and throat, beating in all the wrong places and too hard. She still had her gun in her hand. They walked Duke away and as he passed he wouldn't look at her. There had been no fight. There was no try-anything last minute bravado. He had obediently bent to a symbol of authority and left her on her own.

Chevrons walked toward her slowly. "You'll like it in the barracks. You and the other girls can paint each other's toenails and catch up on all that girl talk. Haven't you missed that?"

Her eyes were hot and she could feel angry tears coming.

He kept his eyes on hers and walked toward her slowly, slowly. She knew he was coming in to disarm her. It was time to make a decision.

"How many?" She asked it again, strangling. "How many? I've seen three women in six months. How many are there?"

"Too many to count." He kept advancing.

"What are their names? The ones you know. Your friends. The ones you like." She wanted him to be telling the truth. Even if it meant living in a military harem, she wanted there to be a bunch of women laughing together somewhere. Someone to read romance novels aloud to, to not be the last one on earth. She could survive that. She could survive anything and come out alright. She thought of the drag king midwife. And of Nettie. She smashed her eyes closed to squeeze the tears out.

"Terri. Mary. Sherry. Carrie. Snow White and Cinderella are there, too. Don't worry about it. You'll see them soon. Come on now."

His voice was low, sweet, cozening. It was the voice she had heard a thousand times before. Come on and do it now. Come on and just give me a little. Come on now. Come on.

She didn't trust herself to bring the gun up. She shot it where it was at with her elbow locked and the bullet hit him in the thigh. He gripped it with both hands and went down. His leg was rigid and he was braying through clenched teeth.

"Fuck you," she said clearly. Some of them started toward her, the others just stared. She has a split second to make the decision, but everything seemed to move very slowly.

Under my chin or into the pumps. Under my chin or into the pumps.

A young-looking guy was almost upon her. She decided there was time for both. She took a shot at the pump furthest from her. She hit it dead on but it had been too long since it had been in service. It flamed, but it didn't explode. The action-movie BOOM never came. She stared at failure a beat too long and the kid tackled her. They both slammed into the bike and they went down on top of it. He pinned her and another guy walked up and calmly kicked in her in the side of the head. She blacked out. Duke separated his shoulder struggling against the men that held him. It was the last thing she saw.

Roxanne woke up in the garrison two days later. Her vision was doubled and the only other person there was a girl. The kid was young and developmentally disabled. She couldn't speak so Roxanne never learned her name. The kid signed constantly, frantically, but the only sign language Roxanne had ever learned was 'please' and 'thank you' and a few obscenities.

The deaf girl was dead in a year. Roxanne lived a long time, but she never saw Duke again. The garrison's radio broadcast kept people coming down the I-5, but it didn't always work. When she died she was still the only woman there.

*****

Dusty woke up a few mornings after she had taken the diary to the sound of Jodi and Honus arguing in the kitchen.

"I don't care! It's too long."

"Sweetheart, I'll be fine. I promise."

"It's two days! Like two whole days! No way!"

Dusty walked out of her bedroom, rubbing her head. They turned to face her when she made it into the kitchen.

"Breakfast is almost ready," Jodi said, turning away.

"Dusty." Honus pulled a kitchen chair around backward and sat facing the table, his legs split around it.

"Mhmm." Dusty opened the window to fill a pan with snow to make coffee.

"I want to go on a two-day raid. Into Ogden. I can make it there and back in two days. There's some stuff we need that I'm not going to find in houses here in Eden. It has to be done."

Jodi did not turn from the stove. "Anything could happen to you. You could crash your snowmobile. Or get lost. Or like murdered by crazy people."

Honus sighed. Jodi walked over and laid a plate in front of Dusty. More powdered eggs. Dusty sighed, then dug in anyway. She got up when the pot on the fire steamed. She made a cup of coffee and sat back down, sipping.

Jodi laid breakfast for herself and Honus. Honus said a blessing and they began to eat in terse silence.

After a little while, Dusty spoke up. "I could go with you."

Honus looked up. Jodi looked at Honus.

"It'd be safer than you going alone. We could look out for each other. I need to try to find another binder, if I can. And there are some things I'd like to have for the birth that we don't have here." She sipped her coffee.

Honus argued first. "We'd have to leave Jodi alone. What if something happened to her? What if the baby…"

Jodi stared at him. "I don't want you to go. I don't want to be alone."

"Would you feel better if Dusty went with me?"

Jodi bit her lower lip and the effect of it was devastating.

"You'd have to stay pretty quiet. And I've been meaning to teach you to use a rifle, anyway. It's only two days." Dusty watched them both. She had cabin fever pretty bad but hadn't considered going that far away.

"Two days at the most. How about it, honey?"

Jodi looked back and forth between the two of them. "Not today, right?"

"No," Honus said brightly. "Maybe in a day or two."

Dusty did show Jodi how to fire a rifle, but she doubted the girl would ever do it. She was too awkward with it, too afraid. Her heart wasn't in it. Dusty thought that if her life were in danger, she might get used to it, but mostly she gave up.

For his part, Honus was very loving toward Jodi before their departure. She ate it up like a lifelong daddy's girl and Dusty tried to spend her time chopping wood or reading in her bedroom. At night, she waited to see if the Obermeyers would share a bedroom, but they didn't.

On the day they had chosen to depart, they got up before dawn. Jodi had drawn all the shutters and shades, as she had been instructed. She would only light the fire at night, and she would sleep with a rifle in her bedroom. She trembled and cried as Honus hugged her goodbye. He tried to kiss her with a little more passion than usual but she pushed him away after a brushing of lips. Dusty ran through symptoms for Jodi to watch for, and told her to take it easy as much as possible.

"There's no one to cook for and the place is spotless. Relax."

Jodi pouted. "But there's nothing to dooooo," she whined.

"Read a book."

Jodi made a face.

She locked the door behind them and they took off just as the day started to turn light. Dusty rode behind Honus, with her hands planted behind her on the block of the seat. When that got uncomfortable, she wrapped her arms around his middle. She tried not to think about their contact and focus on the road. She did not entirely succeed.

The snowmobile was the best possible method of travel. No plows had been out and the road was all but invisible. An equal blanket of snow covered everything and they cut across yards and intersections and fields. They vaguely followed highway signs. Ogden was not far away, and the snowmobile was fast. They made it in no time at all.

They pulled up beside the Ogden mall, and Dusty dismounted. "Why did you tell Jodi it would be two days? We could be back tonight."

Honus grinned at her. "I'm working on a project. Also there's a lot here we can load up. Come on, I have so much to show you!"

As Honus slogged through the snow to the main mall entrance, Dusty realized he must have been here before. Recently.

Honus had made a list. He didn't show Dusty, but they talked about it. He thought she should get her own snowmobile. She didn't think they would find any, but Honus said there were some inside that no one had been able to drag out.

"They're really heavy, but I think we can do it together," he told her excitedly.

He led her forward. The inside of the mall was dark except the middle, where a huge skylight had fallen in under the weight of the snow. Grey daylight shone on the inert escalators.

Dusty shivered a little, both from the cold and from the memory of another mall. "I don't like this," she said.

Honus looked back at her. "Why not?"

"We're trapped inside. And this is a good place to raid. Anyone might come in. Or already be in."

He grinned. "But the missionaries brought everyone who was left in Ogden back to Huntsville."

"Anyone might have come along since."

"Did you see any tracks in the snow at the entrance?"

Snow just keeps coming down. They'd be covered by now. Probably fine. I hope.

She looked behind her, uneasily. "I see your point. I still don't like this." She touched both guns in her waistband.

They walked up the escalators together.

Honus had been right about the snowmobiles. The dealer was upstairs, and had two floor models in the store. He told her that anyone who bought one there would have had it shipped to them from the stockyard and these were just for show.

"Still, they're all here. They'll run. And I've got extra gas in my can outside." The thing was a beast. They pushed it, grunting, onto a wide plastic sled they had gotten at a kid's store. When it finally thumped off its display pedestal, they both lay down on the floor, panting.

The shoved it out on to the main concourse of the upper floor and wheezed while pushing it to the escalator.

"We don't want to push it too hard," Honus said as it slid away from them, down the escalator on its plastic sled. Only a moment and it banged noisily to the floor. Honus gritted his teeth.

"Well, shit." Dusty was disgusted and very tired. The snowmobile lay on its side.

"Let's come back to that," Honus said amiably. "I'm going to go and find some things I wanted for Jodi and for the baby. Will you be ok? Stay on this floor."

"Yeah, I'm ok"

"Yell if you need me." He was already jogging away.

Dusty wandered a little before getting down to business. She missed San Francisco. Everything in this mall and in Utah had a broad, plain-folk feeling. The consumer goods she saw were like the decorations in the house in Eden: folksy, kitschy, cute. She felt stupid missing the big city, but most of what made up the weird heart of her town was the people now missing from it.

She thought of Jack and the places they had gone on dates. She thought of dark absinthe bars and museums and galleries. She thought about restaurants in the city and her stomach cramped on itself though she wasn't hungry. She remembered the rarified tastes, the roasted bone marrow and local vegetables. The artisan cocktails and small-batch cheeses. It all came back in a rush of her former privileged, moneyed life. She remembered how they'd talk about literature and music and hospital politics. They guessed at when their friends would start having kids and disappear from their lives.

She stared at a male mannequin wearing a flannel shirt turned back at the elbows and a low-slung pair of jeans.

"Jack."

She didn't know she had spoken out loud.

More than food or drink, more than hot showers springing miraculously from the wall in the bathroom, more than television and internet and the buzz of strangers; almost more than the feeling of safety and not having to constantly be on guard, she missed conversation. That moment of connection, of being understood that passed easily between equals. She felt her eyes pricking at the thought.

Books in, books out. Read novels, write a diary. Paper in your hands and silence in your mouth. It's not enough.

She turned the corner and found a big corporate bookstore.

The gate was down.

Honus whistled a short, high note some time later that startled her. She poked her head out of the game store she was in.

"You ok?"

"I'm good. You good?"

"Yeah."

Dusty looked back at the shelf in front of her and chose two wooden games she thought might be fun. She moved on to the next store. She really didn't need anything. She had plenty of clothes, they had raided a lot of food. She might try finding some tools at one of the anchor stores downstairs to open or cut a hole in the bookstore gate. Mostly she browsed morosely, feeling an aching nostalgia for a world that seemed very long ago, and utterly absurd in its existence.

In the late afternoon, Honus found her.

"There's a Hickory Farms downstairs that still has a bunch of food. And I think I know where we can sleep." He was grinning broadly.

"What are you so happy about?"

"I found some really neat things for Jodi. But don't tell her! I'm working on a surprise."

On the lower level, Honus had found a store that sold enormous beanbag chairs, big enough to sleep on. They took comforters from a linen store and set up their nests for the night. Then they had dinner at Hickory Farms. Everything was deadly salty, but delicious. Dusty sliced summer sausage with her pocket knife and Honus cut through cheese logs with a piece of string. They put all of it on crackers and watched snow drift in through the hole in the ceiling.

"So how many people do you think are left?" he asked her.

"I'm not sure. I've seen so few it's hard to extrapolate a number. Not many."

"When you were working at the hospital, did you guys know what it was?"

"Not really. We knew what it did, and that we couldn't stop it. Jack, my partner, he had some ideas. He was working in the lab. But nothing they tried worked and a lot of people died."

Honus was quiet for a minute. "A lot of women died in childbirth, didn't they?"

"Yes," she said cautiously. "A lot did."

"Were they already sick?"

She sighed. "Some were. Some seemed to get sick all of a sudden. What I remember of that time is horror, and I don't know if the plague is even still active anywhere."

Honus ate another cracker. Dusty cracked open a soda.

"So, your partner. Like your partner at the hospital, or…?

"My boyfriend, but that word always made me feel like I was in high school again. We lived together, we were partners."

"Oh. Was he a doctor?"

"Clinical pathologist. More of a lab guy than a sawbones. But yes, a doctor."

"Wow. He must have been smart."

"He was. He is. If he's still alive, he is."

"How did you guys lose each other?"

"I got sick. When I got better, he was gone. He probably thought I would die, I thought I was dying. I don't blame him for taking off. I hope he made it to somewhere better."

"Don't you think of finding him? Don't you miss him?"

"Of course I miss him!" She said it a little too sharply. She softened. "I miss him a lot. I miss a lot of people. I had to leave the city, and there's almost no way to find anyone. I don't know how I would even begin to try. What we have now is living, and a way to keep on living. That's it."

"We have more than that. We have the future. Like my son."

He's talking to himself. Repeating his catechism. Not my job to confirm him. Still.

She couldn't look at him. "I really hope you do. For both of you. I really want this birth to go smoothly and the baby to be ok. But you have to be prepared for the possibility that it won't."

"Have you delivered a baby since…"

"Not since the hospital, no. But I heard from a woman who did. It wasn't a good day."

Honus did not ask for details.

Dusty got up and went to a counter on the other side and brought back a couple of Cokes.

"So how did you know you wanted to marry Jodi?"

Honus grinned. "She was just so cute. She was always hanging around, going to my games. I knew she liked me."

Dusty tried not to sound disappointed. "So, do you guys have much in common?"

"Dusty, I know what you're getting at. My dad asked me the same question. Jodi is very childlike. She's simple. But she's really kind and sweet. And she'll make a great mother."

Dusty nodded and drank her coke.

"Did you ever want to marry Jack?"

She shook her head. "We weren't big fans of the institution. I found it oppressive, he found it archaic. Plus, so many of our friends couldn't get married until the laws changed that for a long time it just felt like a farce."

"Oh. Oh. But don't you want to have kids?"

Dusty shrugged. "I caught kids for a living. I got the miracle of life on a daily basis. That was enough."

"But it's not the same as having kids of your own," he protested.

"No, it isn't."

"Do you ever want to have kids?"

She looked at him levelly. He did not intend to be cruel. No one who presses this question does, it's just something they desperately need to nail down about you. To know, and put you down as normal or abnormal.

He waited.

"Let's wait and see how Jodi's birth goes. Let's see if anyone survives childbirth ever again. OK?"

Honus looked at his lap. After a while, he spoke again.

"Is your name really Dusty?"

That surprised her.

"You told the ward that your name was Dusty, because you were pretending to be a man. But Dusty can be a girl's name. I just… I don't think it's your real name. Am I right?"

"No. Yes, I mean you're right. Dusty's not my name."

"So what is your name?"

She felt it again, that same tug of meaning, of power attached to her real name. She could give him another fake, but that would only complicate things with Jodi. She looked at him and felt drawn in, felt the ghost of their bodies pressed together on the ride into town.

"Dusty is fine for now."

He smiled. "I bet I can guess it."

"I bet you can't. Help me cut open this gate."

They dusted the crumbs off their hands and she showed him the bookstore that had locked down. They searched for bolt cutters but didn't find them. He was sorry, she was disappointed. They laid down in their huge beanbags to sleep.

They pulled their bags close, but not close enough to touch.

"Dusty?"

"Yeah."

"What do you miss most?"

She thought for a minute. "People or stuff?"

"People are the obvious answer. What stuff do you miss?"

"The internet. I was a junkie. The sound of traffic. The feeling of safety. What do you miss?"

"Ice cream. I want to find and ice cream maker. Also my mom's dryer, with warm soft clothes to put on. Jodi does her best, but…"

"Yeah, it's not the same. You know what I've been thinking about?"

"What?"

"In a few years, we'll use up all the gas. And the coffee. And the pineapple and chocolate and coconut and all the other shit we brought in from other countries. I'll probably never eat a banana again."

"Jeez, no bananas." He sounded mournful.

"Yeah. I'm gonna miss that."

"Baby food bananas are pretty good. You guys will have to raid it. Might as well give the kid a taste of the lost world before it's gone forever."

Honus didn't say anymore. Dusty reached out, but her fingers found nothing. They slept.

#

Out in the lost world were hundreds of soldiers who had been sent abroad before the end of it all and could not be brought home. In the wilds of Afghanistan and the ancient cities of Iraq, they were making their way. At bases in Europe, they were holding their ground against the locals only by firepower. When that ran out, they would be taken. Peace corps kids in Africa realized they could not swim home, would never see home again. Tourists all over Asia, the Caribbean, stranded in airports, forgotten in consulates lived long enough to face the terror of permanence in strange lands. Cruise ships drifted full of plague dead, a few unlucky souls left alive on some.

Choices made in the final months and weeks of the lost world determined where so many would be marooned. Unfamiliar surroundings contributed to the body count, and the number of people on Earth got smaller and smaller.

In the morning, they tackled the snowmobile again. They got it righted and brought the gas in so they could drive it out the door. It was a newer model than Honus' with all the bells and whistles that the store wanted to show off. Dusty thought she'd have to get used to it, but that it would probably be pretty fun after that.

They had found everything they wanted and more before noon. They sat and ate jerky and salty snacks and dried fruit, sitting on their beanbags.

"So, can I ask you something kind of personal?"

"Sure," Honus said. His face was like an open book.

"Why aren't you and Jodi sharing a bedroom?"

"Oh, that." He reddened. "I was wanting to ask you about that anyway. Jodi thinks that us being… together might hurt the baby."

"Oh is that all? I can tell her that it won't. It's totally ok."

"Ok, that might help. But still…"

"Still what?"

"Jodi's… she's not very… she's never really… enjoyed…" Honus' face was nearly purple.

"She's not into sex? It's ok, Honus. I've been a nurse for a long time, mostly in women's health. There might be an issue that makes it painful for her. Or maybe she's just shy about it because of her upbringing."

"The church teaches us that it's a beautiful, sacred part of marriage and it brings us closer even as it brings us children. I don't think it's that."

"Ok," Dusty said doubtfully. "Does she complain that it's painful?"

"No, not since the first couple of times. I was really gentle, but…" He trailed off.

"Right. And since then?"

"She says she just doesn't feel anything. She's not very… enthusiastic."

Dusty could see that his embarrassment about this was going to be the main barrier to understanding.

"Have you two tried changing positions, or trying… alternate sex acts?"

"Like what?"

She took a deep breath. "Have you tried stimulating your wife orally? Or with your fingers? Women's orgasms are very different from men's. Do you know how she masturbates?"

"Oh, she's never done that."

"Don't be too sure."

"No, I asked her. I wanted to know how I could… you know, make her happy. She said she had no idea, because she had never had one before."

"So maybe you should offer to help her." Dusty felt a small smile starting at the corners of her lips. His face read that this was all very naughty, very far past the line of propriety.

"I… I already kind of suggested that. She was pretty grossed out. I don't know if it's just the pregnancy, but… yeah. She's just not interested."

"Well, she might just not have much of a sex drive. That happens sometimes, and it's normal. But I think it's more likely that she just hasn't discovered what turns her on. You might have to seduce her."

"What? How do I seduce her? She's already my wife."

"Lots of foreplay, lots of touching. Deep kissing. Nipple play. If she's not comfortable with you touching her clitoris, maybe you could find a small battery-powered vibrator. Now there's an endangered species. But it might be enough to get her started. There's a store upstairs that has them."

He got up suddenly, thrashing his way out of the huge beanbag.

"You ok?"

"Yeah. Yeah, I'm fine." He walked out of the store and stood on the concourse a while. When he turned to walk away, she saw the outline of his erection by the dim light of day.

Clinically, she diagnosed it as long celibacy coupled with talking more explicitly about sex than he probably ever had before. In the part of her that was not clinical, she clenched up and throbbed for just a second, everything hot and aching inside her.

*Winter in the Mall*

Can barely stand them. Either one of them. Honus = almost interesting. Right on the edge. Sometimes I can get a whole conversation with him, like tonight. Mostly = goofy about his wife and such an optimist I could vomit. Jodi = so dumb I can hardly stand it. If she wasn't pregnant I'd have dropped her ass off back in Huntsville by now.

But my dreams = fucking them both. Hasn't been that long. But fuck. FUCK.

Going to get my own vibrator before we leave.

*****

They drove back on separate snowmobiles and Dusty was relieved. She got used to it pretty quickly and found that it was capable of terrifying speeds. They stopped at a house near theirs and Honus dropped off one of his bags there.

"To surprise Jodi later. If I bring it in the house, I'll totally give it to her now."

Dusty smiled.

They arrived back home and Jodi had hot soup waiting for them. She was anxious and worried, but they told her the trip had been fine.

*Winter, every day is exactly the same*

Tension = ridiculous. Pretty sure Honus feels it too, but Jodi doesn't have a clue. Every time she's out of earshot, we're talking about sex. How to touch her, how to talk to her, how to turn her on. He says he's not jacking off because it's wrong but I doubt it. Think I'm doing a good job of hiding it, but I'm down. As down as I've ever been. Shit. Trauma, loss, assault, afraid for my life, and yet. Compulsion to fuck is so strong in our species. In all circumstances, always. Remember what it was like when I was with my first girlfriend in college. Was head-over-heels wanting to fuck her all the time. We barely went to class until we both flunked that anatomy test. Ironic. This feels like that. Stir-crazy inevitable come-and-fuck-me crazies. Probably crazy for nothing.

Not Jack not Jack no one is. Hope you're out there, hope you made it. Somewhere. Never find you never find me find me. This is not that.

*****

In the time before time ran out, everyone at UCSF who wasn't sick had been taken by medevac helicopter to the airport and then flown to a CDC-FEMA camp established at a base in the Ozark Mountains. Dr. John Eberhard (Jack to everyone but his mother) was among them. He showed no sign of fever. He had to be sedated. He would not leave his lab voluntarily. He awoke as the plane landed bumpily in Missouri. They replaced his equipment. They did not replace her. For days he worked at convincing himself that she was dead. She must be dead. There were four women in the camp. Fifty five men. No children. He was the only medical professional who had been evacuated from the west coast. Everyone he met was from the south, a few from New York. They worked together with the samples that the CDC provided them. Quarantine was absolute. In a month, they isolated it. They knew its DNA and thought they knew its origin. They developed a vaccine and a FEMA crew flew it into St. Louis to find infected persons on whom to test it. The crew did not return.

Jack intentionally infected himself without telling a soul. He did not develop symptoms. He confessed his breach to Dr. Austin Calhoun, a man from Atlanta who had seen three daughters into death. Calhoun nodded without judgment. He later did the same. Both men were immune.

It was nearly summer before they found an infected young girl in St. Louis. She was pregnant. She would not speak. They took every possible precaution and administered the vaccine. When she died, they took the baby by C-section. A small girl, born grey. DOA. They debated whether the two of them had already been too far gone before the test began. They debated whether the vaccine had killed them. Mother and child were autopsied and no conclusions could be agreed upon.

The day after he sliced the infant's brain to be pressed between glass, Jack calmly administered a fatal overdose of morphine to himself.

His last thought was that to die in such peace in a world like this was the most privileged and selfish act he had ever committed.

# Chapter Nine

THE BOOK OF HONUS OBERMEYER
CONTAINING THE STORY OF THE FIRST HIVE
AS SCRIBED BY THE UNNAMED MIDWIFE

*Day 53*

We've been with Amanda in her hive, as she calls is, for two days. They caught us that night on the roof and brought us here. They forced us to drink strong drink, and then there was dancing with strange drum music. I was so frightened. I broke the Word of Wisdom. I was stripped nude and force-fed more alcohol. I was given a pipe to smoke and I smoked it. I think it was marijuana. It smelled like the kids I knew were trouble in high school. The feeling of it seemed to go on for days and days. I lost track of time. I forgot who I was. I woke up sick and with my mouth dry and my head pounding. I thought I would die, but I did not.

Amanda is a tall, beautiful girl. She has long blonde hair and bright green eyes. She wears clothing that barely exists, like bikini underwear and see-through dresses. I can always see her breasts. I try to look away. She doesn't speak to us, she speaks to all the men as though they were one person. There are about twenty men here. They are all on drugs. Most of them have tattoos. I don't know what this place is but there are no windows and there are four or five stages in the room. Maybe it's some kind of theater. They barely eat food, preferring to drink and smoke. Langdon is in a haze constantly. I tried to leave and drag him out with me, but a group of the men stopped me. They were making this terrible noise. I'm terrified.

*Day 54*

I was called in to speak with Amanda in private. She made me kneel in front of her as she lay naked on a couch. I tried not to look, but it was such a trial. She asked me where we were from. I couldn't think of any reason not to tell her the truth, so I did. She seemed very happy that we were LDS. She said we would be her 'prettiest boys.' I showed her my ring and told her I was married right away.

She said that all the other girls had died and she was all that was left. I told her not my girl.

She got up and told me to sit on her couch. She traded me places and knelt in front of me, her breasts against my inner thighs. I fought temptation, I struggled like Jacob struggled with the angel. She tried to unzip my pants but I stopped her. I told her no.

She said she was the queen of the hive and she needed more drones to bring her honey. Nothing about that made sense to me, but I didn't want her. I wanted to go home.

She seemed to go blank then. She had been all sweet-talk and seduction until the moment I said no, then she went totally blank like she had no feelings at all. She told me to get out and send in the other one. I asked her if she meant Elder Langdon. She laughed a little and showed me a tiny blue pill with a dolphin stamped on it. I shook my head and she put it in her own mouth. I walked out of the room and the guards were already pushing Langdon through the door.

I waited in the main stage-room with the other men. They were all drinking alcohol or taking drugs. It seemed like that was what they did all day. Some of them were dancing on the stages using the poles. They all seemed to be naked or on their way there. Some of them were having sex with one another. I've never imagined anything like that in my life, even on those occasions when I was tempted to view pornography and gave in. I didn't know where to look. I thought I might be able to get away while they were all distracted, but then Amanda burst out of her room into their midst. She held Langdon's hand. He was naked.

She said something like, "Drones! Today a new bee joins your number!" They all hooted and clapped and some of them buzzed. I tried to get Langdon to look me in the eye, but he was obviously high as a kite.

I asked him if he had taken the dolphin from her.

I am the dolphin, he told me.

Amanda led him to the largest central stage and told him today was his day. She laid him down and straddled him and I tried to run away then but I couldn't believe this freaking abomination was really happening. Every man in the room rushed the stage and I could see them reaching for her with their dicks out, trying to jam them anywhere near her. They became an inhuman pile of the most disgusting sex I can imagine.

I started to back away when one of them grabbed me. It all happened so fast that I barely understood what was happening. He wrestled me to the floor, trying to kiss the back of my neck. I could feel his erection against me and I just panicked. He was so rough and out of control and I tried to pull away but he just kept on. I tried to turn around and push him off me, I ended up elbowing him straight in the eye. I kicked him hard once he was off me. My heart was hammering and I couldn't even see straight.

I ran. I found the room where they had put my clothes and my pack and I got as dressed as I could and ran for the back door. The whole back side of that building was like a maze of little rooms and hallways and there was no light. Eventually I hit a door that burst open and I couldn't believe it was daytime.

Out back there was a dumpster overflowing with dead bodies. Some of them lay half out of it, like laundry hanging out of the hamper. More of them were piled on the ground. Live bodies were piled up inside and dead bodies were piled up outside.

I threw up. The smell and the drugs and everything I had just been through was just too much. I ran away, still vomiting, just wanting to get out of there. I didn't stop until I got to a little house and broke a window to get in.

I prayed for Elder Langdon. I don't know if he made the choice or the choice was made for him. I just know I can't go back for him. Never ever could I go back.

*****

Dusty sat back from the book and stared at the candle. Her mouth was dry. It made sense that Honus had not wanted to share this. She was more than halfway through his diary.

She slept in and woke up to the sound of Honus splitting wood outside. There was more than enough wood on the side of the house. It had become a signal between them that meant 'come outside and talk to me.'

Jodi was where she always was: in the kitchen. Dusty looked at her posture, the way she held the lordotic curve in the small of her back with her hands; the way she waddled. It would be soon.

They had everything Dusty thought they might possibly need. She had taught both Jodi and Honus to time her contractions with a watch they had brought back from the mall. She approached Jodi and asked permission before palpating her belly.

"He's kicking all the time! He stopped doing somersaults, though."

Dusty's hands found the baby's head. The kid was turned and faced Jodi's spine. He was ready. "I don't think he has enough room to do that anymore. How are you feeling?"

Jodi fidgeted. "Ok. Bored, mostly. And anxious. I want to have the baby already. Like meet him and hold him. You know?"

"I know." They had brought home formula in case Jodi couldn't breastfeed. They had hidden it from her, in case things went wrong or she felt insulted by it. "No pain or weird feelings?

Nightmares?"

"Yeah like crazy nightmares! Like I lost him or someone is trying to take him from me. All the time!"

"That's pretty common. If you get scared in the middle of the night, you should go wake up Honus. He can comfort you, and help you get back to sleep."

Dusty had tried suggesting before that Jodi seek her husband's comfort in the middle of the night. She had tried innocuous ways and explicit ways. She had tried to ask Jodi about sex. She had been met with suspicion and disgust. It was not a subject they could talk about.

Jodi pulled back from her now and returned to the business of cooking. "Oatmeal soon. With raisins or craisins. Your choice."

"We got any nuts?"

"Yeah I forgot you like them. Some walnuts."

"Good." Dusty went outside.

Honus swung the axe over his head and brought it down in a neat arc. He had shucked down to his over shirt, and Dusty could see the wing of muscles down his side flex and extend.

Latissimus dorsi, whispered the part of her brain that was always preparing for exams in nursing school. She sat on the woodpile.

"How's Jodi?"

"She's fine. But I do think it will be soon."

Honus' face lit up. "I can't wait."

"I can wait forever. They're both healthy right now, I wish I knew that would stay that way."

"Don't worry so much. Have faith."

Dusty said nothing, hoping the moment would pass.

"Don't you have any faith at all? Weren't you raised with any?"

"My parents weren't religious."

"Weren't you ever curious what it was all about?"

"I had a phase in college when I went to church with a bunch of my friends to see what they were so crazy about. I didn't find anything I wanted."

"Did you ever have a feeling like the presence of God?"

Dusty thought about storms gathering over the lake before she had had to kill to defend it. She remembered days at the beach and hikes in the woods. She thought about the raw wonder of birth and swiftly her mind plunged into memories of orgasm. Her college girlfriend scream-spasming with Dusty's whole fist inside her. Coming together with Jack at the best of times, like an electric circuit completing itself. The birth of the baby approached and all Dusty could think about was sex. She was already out of batteries.

"I've felt something," she finally said.

Honus put the axe down and started to stack wood against the house. "Do you know the Bible?"

"Pretty well, yeah. I had to take a class in it as an undergrad."

"How well do you know the life of Jesus?"

She sighed. They had had moments before when she had the distinct feeling he was working on her. She hated it, especially that he thought she couldn't tell. She looked back in the window to see if breakfast was ready yet. It was not.

"Pretty well. I could tell the whole story if I needed to."

"Did you know he was married?"

"I know some people think so." This was already tiresome.

"Did you know he had two wives?" Honus looked at her mischievously.

"What?"

Honus put one leg up on the woodpile. He had her full attention. "So you know the story where Jesus is teaching in the home of two sisters, Mary and Martha. And Mary sits and listens to Jesus talking while Martha works in the kitchen. And Martha gets mad and comes out and complains to Jesus like, 'Hey Jesus! This isn't fair! Make her come help me.' And Jesus tells her that Mary made her own choice, and they're both good ones."

Dusty nodded.

"So some people think that it was his house, and they were his wives. That's why they acted like he was in charge of them. Makes sense, right? So when my ancestors practiced plural marriage, they were following in the footsteps of the son of God."

Dusty nodded again. "So are you saying now that there are so many more men than women, you'd like Jodi to find another husband or two?"

How does that sound? Try it on that way.

"What? No! I was saying that if you—"

Jodi opened the door. "Breakfast!"

When she was gone again, Dusty turned back to Honus. "I'm not all torn up about polygamy. It doesn't bother me at all as long as it's what people choose. But don't you think it's a little ridiculous with the way things are now to suggest that one man should have a couple of wives? Really, it's more likely that if they have a choice, women will collect multiple mates." She wasn't alluding to Amanda, but she could tell that's what he was thinking.

He straightened up and headed inside.

It was only afterward that she realized he had been coming on to her the only way he knew how.

*****

A few more monotonous days and he got over it. They sat up late one night, talking after Jodi had gone to bed. Dusty had made them hot chocolate and they sat on the sofa, staring into the fire.

"So some women do enjoy sex, huh? It's not just a myth made up by pornographers?" He smiled lopsidedly at her.

Dusty snorted. "They really do. Jodi doesn't mean to hurt your feelings. She really loves you. I can't figure out why, but she's just not interested."

"But you enjoy it. Or you used to, when you were with Jack. Right?"

"Yeah, I really did. With Jack and with Cassie and with Dana and with Andrew…"

He blushed. "You've had a lot of partners… and I know some of them were women…"

"I come from somewhere very different than you two," she said gently.

He nodded, getting a hold of himself. "I know, I know. It's just… it's really different." He slugged his cocoa as if it would give him courage. "You know, Jodi is grossed out that you were ever with a woman. She's worried that you might look at her… that way."

Dusty drank, too. "Yeah, straight girls worry that a lot. She's got nothing to fear from me. I hope she doesn't think I'm perving out on examining her."

"Nah, she's really glad that you can take care of her and the baby. She kind of keeps it separate."

They sat in the crackling warmth.

"Don't you want to know if I think it's gross?"

"Not really." Old anger flared up.

What's the point, what's the point? Why fight about this now when it barely matters anymore?

"Well, I don't. I never bought the church line about marriage. I do think there's something special about temple marriage, but legal marriage is something else. I don't think it's gross." He looked at her expectantly.

Pin a ribbon on me. I'm so progressive.

"What if it's two guys?" She was not in a ribbon-pinning mood.

Honus sucked a breath in between his teeth. "That's harder

for me to understand, because I think guys are gross and hairy and I've never wanted one. But it's none of my business if another guy does. As long as it's not me." Once more, he tried for the ribbon.

"Well then. How evolved of you. I expect a number of men will find themselves attracted to each other in this brave new world. What a surprise it will be." She wanted to discuss his diaries with him, badly. She hinted all the time but he never suspected.

"Do you like guys better? Or girls?"

Not that evolved.

"It's not like that. I like people. They come with the bodies they come with."

"I've never met anyone like you." His fingers had crept across the cushion between them and came to rest on hers.

She was somewhere between laughing in his face at the cheesiness of his line and climbing into his lap and fucking him right then. It was a strange place. She leaned a little toward him, not feeling like it was a conscious decision, but only the drawing of one magnet to the other.

"Yeah, you're new for me, too."

His fingers slid over hers and then laced between them. She burned.

"Honus?"

It was Jodi. Her voice was muffled by the closed door but it made him jump anyway. "What's wrong?" He ran down the hall and stood beside her door.

"Nothing's wrong, but can you bring me some water?"

"Of course, honey. Of course. Be right there."

He did not look at Dusty as he crossed into the kitchen. She got up without a word and went to bed. She knelt facing her headboard and stroked her clit between two fingers maybe four times before she came. Afterward, she touched her guns and lay down and fell asleep.

## THE BOOK OF HONUS OBERMEYER
## AS SCRIBED BY THE UNNAMED MIDWIFE

*Day 64*

I've been without a companion for more than ten days now. I have decided to push onward and serve my mission fully before returning.

I thought I was lonely when Langdon was distant, but this is much worse. I've never felt so alone in my life. I'm praying to meet some people in Denver, but I also fear meeting anyone. Please Heavenly Father, please help me find the people I've been called to. Let the spirit guide them if you would have them seek me. I'm not even asking for a golden contact. Just nice normal people who I can talk to. Maybe even someone to bring back with me.

The terrain is becoming mountainous and the nights are very cold. The road into Denver is not in good shape. There are car wrecks on the other side and dead people in cars on the shoulder heading in. I saw animals a few days ago. A herd of antelope first, followed by a couple of moose. I've never seen an animal that big outside of a zoo. It was a little scary, but I am glad to see them. It means there is something we can hunt for fresh meat. I've never learned to do that, but I bet there are other elders who know how.

*Day 70*

I've gotten terrible about keeping my missionary journal, but there's so little to tell. I eat alone, whatever I can find. I read scriptures alone, I pray alone. I sleep alone, I wake up alone. I walk toward Denver. I am really hoping to find a bicycle.

*Day 75*

I found a bicycle. It's so much faster, I can't believe how much ground I have covered. By the map, I am very close to Denver. Thank you, Heavenly Father. I know you laid my path for me and there is a reason for every part of it. Please see me safely to the temple so that I may find my people.

*Day 81*

(This page is just the lyrics to "You Fill up My Senses" written out with some hymn after it)

*Day 89*

What a day.

I reached the street that the temple was on and saw that most of the area had burned down. The street was clear though, so I pedaled as fast as I could. I couldn't see it. The houses around it are all on twisty streets, so I turned and turned again trying to get to it. When it finally came into view, I hit the brakes and got off. I walked toward the back fence. There was something behind it that looked like it used to be a gazebo. I walked around the fences to the front entrance.

I could tell it used to be a beautiful temple. It had burned almost completely. Everything that used to be white had gone black. The garden in front was torched and the fountain and pools were empty and dry. The structure still stood, even the steeple was still up. I decided to go in.

I went through the baptismal room. It was empty, but the water had gone sour and cloudy. The whole building reeked. Aside from the fire, I couldn't tell if anything bad had happened. I went upstairs through the different rooms. I could tell it used to be a splendid, restful place. It broke my heart to see it burned and abandoned like this. I thought there would be signs here that someone had taken care of it.

All the way up in the sealing room, there were people. They had all been burned. There was nothing left to tell who they were. Maybe ten of them lay around the altar, black and twisted. May Heavenly Father give them peace. At least they died near to Him.

I had to find something to bring back with me, to show that I had been here and there was no reason to return. I found the cover of the white visitor's book, badly burned but the embossed letters still visible. It crumbled in my hand but I got a big piece of it. I wrapped it in one of my garments and put it in my bag.

There's nothing here. There's nothing here or anywhere.

*Day 95*

I sat with the map and planned my route back. I don't want to go back the way I came. There's a northern route through Wyoming that will get me back to Huntsville. I'll head that way.

*Day 115*

Wyoming is desolate country. I still have my bicycle. There's nothing to tell.

*Day 124*

I am reflecting much of the time. I search, ponder, and pray. If I can even desire to believe, and let this desire work on me, I can still have room in me for the word. Alma 32:27. I have only myself to think about. The stars are brighter than I've ever seen. I can see the Milky Way. The night is immense and majestic and I stare at the stars and I think.

I think about my mission in Canada and how much I complained. How lucky I was then! I think about the ice cream cooler I found in that gas station, all moldy goo with papers and labels floating in it. That almost made me cry like a baby. But I'm a man, so I ate some pretzels and thought about my wife. What if she's pregnant? We were together for a week, but one time is enough. I might come home to a baby on the way. My beautiful Jodi, carrying my child. What a blessing in these terrible times.

I am not really on a mission anymore. I found what I was meant to find, even though it was an empty victory. There is no one to help or minister to. There is only me, on my bicycle, in the wilderness. I'm not in the wilderness like Nephi was. I don't have to eat locusts or cast out demons. I just have to deal with myself. But there are demons in my wilderness. The wilderness is in my heart. I guess my demons are my nightmares.

I have decided to tell them Elder Langdon died on the road. I know it's terrible to lie, but the truth is worse. Kurt Avery Langdon died serving his mission for the Church of Jesus Christ of Latter-Day Saints. I didn't know him well. He was from Eden, and I didn't meet him until we refugeed in from Ogden. He was a man of few words. His parents had died, and he came in with a group but I could tell he was alone. I hoped we would talk on the mission and get to know each other, but I think he had already given up. I wish I knew him better. I wish I could have dragged him out of that terrible place. For what it's worth, I'll tell people he ended better than he did. That's my gift to you, companion.

* * * * *

Oh Honus. Only a little bit left. Will finish it tomorrow night. Understanding him better now.

Honus had taken to raiding almost every day. Both Jodi and Dusty assumed that he was trying to avoid being around the house, and both of them took it personally.

Dusty did not want to talk to Jodi. She was jealous and angry and anxious and guilty and annoyed with her. Jodi pouted at being left behind, at being bored, and grew testy and snappish.

Dusty listened to Jodi washing another thing that did not need to be washed and heard her hitch her breath a few times. They had not spoken in hours.

"Are you having contractions?"

"No, I'm not having contractions, mother."

Another few hours of silence ensued.

* * * * *

When Honus returned in the evening, Dusty watched with disgust as Jodi flung herself at him, demanding to know where he had gone. He came back from many of these all-day trips with little more than a few candles or a can of Crisco. His excuses were wearing thin, and he knew it.

"A man's got to work, honey."

Dusty walked down the hall to get away from them, but she left her bedroom door open. She didn't know when she had begun to eavesdrop. Between listening to their private conversations and reading Honus' diary, she could hardly stand herself.

"Are you avoiding me?"

"No, sweetheart. I just have things to do."

"Like what things? It's not like you have a job! You don't even take a rifle to go hunting. What the heck do you do all day? I'm so bored and alone!"

"You're not alone. You have Dusty."

"I don't want to talk to Dusty. She's boring."

Dusty stifled a laugh.

"Darling, you have to trust me. There's something that I'm working on. A surprise."

Jodi's voice lost all trace of unhappiness. "A surprise! Really?"

"Really. Yes. It's gonna be ready soon, but you have to be patient with me, ok?"

"Ok baby."

Dusty could hear their chaste kiss go smack. Her face burned.

## THE BOOK OF HONUS OBERMEYER
## AS SCRIBED BY THE UNNAMED MIDWIFE

*Day 136*

Thank you Heavenly Father for putting these men in my path. I am grateful beyond measure to have met them.

I came through Laramie two days ago and on the outskirts of town I met Will and Renny Tucker. They're brothers and best friends and they are good and decent men.

They came out to meet me in the road with their hands

outstretched. They did everything they could to show me they meant no harm. I was still afraid, but I spoke to them anyway. I told them I was a traveler and a missionary and I was on my way back to Utah. They said they had lived here all their lives and had no plan to leave it. They invited me back to their farm, so I went.

They have cattle, oh man do they have cattle! They said they rounded up all they could care for and set the rest free. I couldn't even count how many they were. They showed me their patches for vegetables and fruit orchards but it's too cold now for much of anything. They had a few pumpkins still out. They invited me for dinner and I stayed.

The Tucker brothers live like pioneers. They dry and can and preserve all they have. Their home looks just right with kerosene lamps and they are comfortable in the silence. The only thing they miss are the women in their lives. I wasn't sure that they'd want to talk about it, but they did some.

Will's wife died right away, as soon as the plague reached Laramie. Renny's wife lived through it without showing any symptoms but then died in childbirth, and the baby with her. Renny showed me the grave. It was still pretty fresh. I thought of Jodi, and my heart was troubled.

Despite their tragedy and the way the world has changed, they treated me like family. We had a good dinner and Will played guitar and both Renny and I sang along. It was so good, Lord. Like something I lost a long time ago turning up unexpectedly.

Another blessing- the Tuckers told me where I could—

* * * * *

"What are you doing?"

Dusty's eyes snapped up. Honus had gotten up out of bed and come into the living room without her noticing.

She didn't answer.

"Why do you have my journal? Are you copying it? What the heck are you doing? How could you?"

His voice was rising. Dusty felt her face grow hot. She slowly closed the cover of Honus' diary and tried to figure out what to say.

"I can't believe that you'd… how would you like it if I read your diary? Don't you understand that it's private?"

"Honus, I'm sorry. I'm really sorry, I shouldn't have—"

"What can you possibly have to say for yourself? How do you explain this?"

Jodi was in the room before either of them knew it. "What are you two yelling about?" Her face changed from sleepy to suspicious. "Why are you both up in the middle of the night? What's going on?"

Honus stared at Dusty. She knew he didn't want Jodi to know the diary even existed. She tried to think of a quick lie, but he beat her to it.

"It's the surprise. I got up to check on it, but I didn't know Dusty was still awake, writing in her diary. She scared me. But come on, I want to show you both."

The two women followed Honus out into the front yard. He

had shoveled the walk and it wasn't quite a clear night, but the only clouds were low, grey wisps.

They looked around, trying to spot the surprise. Honus smiled and said "Just wait."

They stood outside a few more minutes. None of them were really dressed for the cold, and before long they were shivering.

"Honus, I'm going to go back inside. I'm like freezing." Jodi's teeth were chattering. Honus went to her and put his arms around her. With one finger pointed to the sky, he said, "Look."

All three of them looked up. A small sliver was cut off the edge of the blazing full moon.

"I don't get it." Jodi sounded disappointed.

"It's an eclipse," Dusty said. "If we had an almanac—"

"We do. I've been waiting for this. I know what day it is." Honus beamed.

Dusty smiled at him. It was a small thing, but they had talked about how odd it was to have lost track of the date. This would put them back on the calendar, for whatever that was worth.

"Is that the surprise?" Jodi sounded beyond disappointed, sulky.

"Only part." Honus kissed the end of her nose and she wrinkled it at him. They all went back inside.

"So guess what day it is!" Honus could barely hold still. He had pulled the Farmer's Almanac out of his pocket and folded the front cover around backwards to the eclipse page.

"I think it's January. Late January." Dusty tried to remember the last time she had taken a stab at the date in her journal.

"What do you think, sweetheart?"

Jodi rolled her eyes. "I don't know. How about like February? Then it might be spring soon."

Honus couldn't contain his excitement. "Nope. Today is December 23rd. In two days, it'll be Christmas."

Jodi lit up like a child. "Oh my heck! Christmas!"

Oh my heck.

It was Dusty's turn to be disappointed, but she masked it with her pleasure at knowing the date.

"That's cool."

"I think we should have a real Christmas! I've been preparing for it for a while. You'll see. I'm going to go get the stuff that I found." With that, Honus was putting on his coat and scarf and dashing out the door.

As soon as he was gone, Jodi turned to Dusty. "I bet he got us presents!"

Dusty had not thought of that. "Wow. Yeah you're probably right. I'm going out for a bit, too. Will you be ok?"

"Totally!" Jodi was already heading for the kitchen.

"What are you doing?"

"I want to make popcorn and string it! And paper chains! And decorations!"

"Jodi, it's still the middle of the night. You should go back to sleep. We can do all that in the morning."

"Oh." She deflated, but only a little.

"Go on back to bed. I'll lock you in."

Dusty went to her diary and closed it. Then she thought about it and decided to hide it under the couch. She put Honus' in the pocket of her coat to put it back in the saddle bag of the snowmobile. She grabbed a rifle and locked the door behind her. She walked for a mile in the weirdly fractured moonlight, then left their trail for the woods.

Jodi thought she was too excited to sleep. She dreamt about a five year old girl who called her mama and kept losing limbs as she played. She woke just before dawn to the sound of the rifle firing.

Honus had gone completely overboard with the madness of Christmas. He lost all restraint over the idea that he could bring home anything without having to pay for it. He dragged a sled back to the house that was weighted down with gifts, then went back for another. He got home and found Jodi asleep, Dusty missing, and an empty rifle slot in the gun case. He looked around for his journal and didn't find it. He resolved not to worry.

He set up an artificial tree with battery-powered LED lights and switched it on. The glow filled the room and he found he had a lump in his throat. He swallowed hard and began shoveling presents underneath the tree. When he came to a small box, he opened it and found an ornament marked "Baby's First Christmas." It was dated two years ago, since no new ones had been made. New ornaments. Not new babies, he told himself. He hung it on the tree and then he did cry. He sat on the couch looking at the tree and the pile of presents, wiping his eyes. He heard the rifle go off, but he wasn't afraid. A sense of wonderful rightness had come over him.

Jodi walked out into the room, tying her robe. "What was that?"

"I think Dusty's got a surprise, too. Merry Christmas, honey."

Jodi clapped her hands like a little girl at the sight of the presents under the tree.

Dusty came back an hour later. She was very cold and her cheeks were bright red. She carried a huge dead turkey.

"Where did you get that?" Honus beamed at her.

"Santa Claus gave it to me. Do either one of you know how to get the feathers off?"

They conferred. Dusty had seen in movies a method of dunking the bird in boiling water and plucking from there. Jodi refused the job as disgusting, but said she would cook it. Dusty told Honus that if he could pluck it, she would gut it. It took Honus the better part of the morning, but he finally got it clean. Jodi announced that she couldn't roast the whole bird without an oven, but she thought she knew what to do. When it was gutted and clean, she had Dusty cut it into inelegant pieces and pack the pieces in snow. Jodi promised it would be just as good as a whole roast turkey.

Jodi spent Christmas Eve stringing popcorn, as she had promised. While she popped it, Honus approached Dusty.

"Do you still have it?"

"I put it back in the saddlebag. Honus, I'm so sorry. I just had to know. It's no excuse, and I know it was a terrible breach of trust. I'm sorry."

"I forgive you," he said formally. "But I am still upset. I feel…"

"Violated?"

"Yeah."

They stared at each other for a minute, then Honus went out to the snowmobile. He came back in and held his journal over the fire. He stood without moving.

"Don't do that."

He didn't answer.

"It's your story. There's nothing in there you need to be ashamed of. It's… just don't. Keep it. Leave it for someone. Give it to me, or to anybody."

"This is supposed to be my personal scripture." His hand dropped a little, nearer to the flames. Dusty stared, but didn't move.

"It's just full of my failure and the sick things I saw." He stared into the fire. "And did."

"You didn't do anything, Honus. You stumbled into something very weird and deadly, and you got out alive. You should be proud."

Honus shook his head, but didn't answer.

Dusty stood up and took it from him, gently. "You'll never see it again. Jodi will never know. It'll be safe. Your… personal scripture. I'll add it to mine."

He turned to face her and they were close enough to kiss. He looked into her eyes like he was searching for something. She reached out and patted his shoulder, looking away.

She hid his diary in her room. They did not speak of it again.

* * * * *

Predictably, Jodi begged to be allowed to open one present the night before Christmas.

"Just one? Please can I open just one?" She wheedled and Honus smiled at her like an indulgent father. Dusty rolled her eyes.

"Ok, but I get to pick which one."

"Ok. Ok ok ok!" Jodi patted her belly excitedly. "The baby's excited too, I can feel it!"

Honus walked to the pile of presents and took two off the top. "One for you," he put it in Jodi's hands. "And one for you." He dropped it into Dusty's lap and she stared at it. "What's this?"

"It's a present, doofus." Honus gave her his lopsided grin. He went back and picked up a third. "And this one's for me, but it's from Santa."

Jodi had already ripped hers open. A hideous red plaid nightgown unfolded. The collar was white lace and it was the dowdiest most old-lady garment Dusty had ever seen. Jodi burst into tears.

"Christmas pajamas! Just like my parents used to do!" She sobbed into her nightgown. Honus came and sat beside her and held her. His package contained a coy pajama set in matching red plaid.

Dusty opened her package as well and found a navy blue set

of pajamas. She was shocked by how tasteful and simple they were. She eyed the two of them, caught up in a moment of comfort. She had not celebrated Christmas as a child, and this moment was not the same for her. But she saw that she was being included. And that Honus had chosen well for her. She got up and went to her room to change.

She put on the pajamas and looked in the mirror. They were softer, nicer than anything she had worn in months. Even with her hair cut brutally short, she looked and felt suddenly very feminine. This came with a thrill of danger and a sudden driving need to display herself to Honus. She walked back out to see them.

"They're lovely. Thank you." She waited until he looked her over.

"Mine's better!" Jodi got laboriously off the couch and soon she was modeling her nightgown, too. It hid any trace of her figure and covered her from neck to ankles. She was however, radiantly pregnant. Dusty and Honus both smiled at her. He got into his and the three of them sat and drank cocoa and stared at the tree. When it started to snow, the Obermeyers began to sing.

Dusty joined in on the songs she knew, but most of them she didn't. It was a good moment. She was part of it enough to enjoy it, and she felt attractive in her navy pajamas. She and Honus shared snatches of eye contact. He broke them before she did.

They went to bed late.

In the morning, Dusty woke to the sound of Jodi knocking excitedly. She obviously couldn't wait to get started. She put on a cinnamon cake to bake and made juice from a powdered mix. Jodi lowered herself heavily to the floor and parked in front of the tree, waiting.

Dusty stumbled out slowly and set about making coffee. She was glad, every day that neither of them partook of her morning ritual. The coffee would last so much longer if only she was drinking it.

"Come on, guys!"

Honus came and sat beside her and rubbed his hands together. Dusty came and sank down beside them, smiling sleepily.

"Alright, let's do this."

Honus started with the smallest packages. Jodi opened a pair of fat diamond earrings and followed it up with a heavy gold bracelet. A hoard of very expensive jewelry began to collect in front of her. Honus followed it with a beautiful jewelry box and Jodi could not stop exclaiming all over it. She put it carefully aside and moved on to the next boxes. She unwrapped a pair of very expensive headphones and looked at them.

"What are these for?"

"You'll see."

Dusty watched, sipping her coffee.

Jodi's next packages were a series of DVD sets of some of her favorite television shows. Her face crumpled a little. "This is just mean."

"Come on, honey. Would I do that to you?" He pushed a large

box toward her and she opened it with some reluctance.

Dusty craned her neck to see inside the box. It contained a solar backpack and a huge case of rechargeable batteries. Jodi looked confused and not at all mollified. Honus followed it with a small battery-operated DVD player.

"See? You have TV to watch. And all your favorite shows! And now you won't be bored for a long time, and we can always track down more movies."

Jodi threw her arms around him, then shrank as if she were in pain.

"Contraction." Dusty set down her coffee.

"No, no it's ok. I've had a couple. They're not getting like any faster." Honus helped her up off the floor and she headed to the kitchen to check on breakfast.

When she was out of the room, Honus pushed a heavy cardboard box in front of Dusty.

"I got something for you, too."

"TV for Jodi is the best gift for me." She smiled.

"No, really." He nudged the box again.

Dusty pulled the flaps of the box open and Honus took Jodi's batteries outside into the sun to charge.

The box was full of books. Some of them she had read before, but most she had not. They all bore stickers from an unfamiliar library in a town she did not know. They were all generally in the vein of books she liked and she was surprised to see he had been paying attention. She was touched, and terribly guilty.

Honus came back in. "Do you get it?"

"Yeah, they're all books that I'll like. This is very thoughtful, thank you so much."

He smiled again and shook his head. "No, you don't get it yet. I'll give you a minute." He walked into the kitchen.

Dusty looked back into the box and scanned over the covers. She tried to find a pattern or see the books in a new way. She reached in and shifted them around. Then she got it.

All the authors were women.

Dusty sat down on the floor with her head on the box and cried.

* * * * *

Jodi had been right about the turkey. She took the hacked-up pieces that Dusty had butchered for her and browned them beautifully in her cast iron skillet. She served the bird with a pot of mashed potatoes she had made from a box of flakes, canned yams, fresh bread, and apple pie. She had even made pan gravy. She lit candles on the table and called them to dinner with shining eyes.

Honus gave a long and heartfelt prayer. For unto us a child is born. Dusty kept her eyes open and saw Jodi have another contraction.

Christmas dinner was delicious.

* * * * *

As soon as her batteries were charged, Jodi loaded the DVD player and set up a new batch to charge and arranged herself on the couch with pillows and blankets and pulled on her headphones.

Dusty and Honus washed the dishes together.

"That was an incredibly thoughtful gift. I'm blown away. I don't know how to thank you."

"I was just in the library and thinking how long it might be before there are new books published. And if any of them will be by women, ever again. And I knew it would matter to you."

"It did. It does."

They washed and dried. Their hands touched, soapy and wet.

"I'm sorry again. About reading your diary. I really am. I just couldn't help myself."

"I kind of thought of joking about it. Like I brought you some new books so you'll stop reading the ones you shouldn't." He laughed a little.

"I'm sorry about your companion. That must have been terrifying."

"It was. I have nightmares sometimes. About that... Well, you know."

"I know. I have nightmares, too."

The dishes were done. The smell of turkey and pie still hung in the warm room.

"I didn't mean it about reading yours. I wouldn't do that to you."

"I know you wouldn't." She was still hiding it.

"I do wonder sometimes what I might find, though." Honus hung up the dish towel he had been using and walked out of the room.

Find me. You might find me.

# Chapter Ten

*December 26*

Jodi went into labor early this morning. Knew it was coming on, so just watched. Going to have a bad time.

*December 27*

She's exhausted. Only two fingers dilated. Walked her until she cried and begged to lie down. On her side now. Have misoprostol but so far she's refused it. Can't c-section, she'd never survive. Sent Honus in to talk her into the drugs if he can. Ate something. Gonna lay my head down for a few minutes and then go back in there.

*December 28*

Fucking mess.

Knew it would end this way. Fucking knew it. Don't know why I let their hope get to me. Stupid.

Two feet of snow outside and frozen ground, we can't even bury the body. They named it. No point in writing it down. No point in naming it. She was right, it was a boy. No point no point.

Can't talk them into cremation. Told Honus the kid can't be in the house, and if we cover it with snow or put it in a box, animals may find it. He just about puked when I said it, but wouldn't budge on the idea of burial.

Jodi lost a lot of blood. Hard birth. Repaired the tearing while she was passed out, then gave her a shot to kill the pain and put her out. She didn't consent to it. Don't give a shit. Needs to rest.

*New Year's Day*

Honus and I cremated the baby last night. He had some time alone with the body while I built the pyre. We did it down the road a ways so that Jodi won't see. He's going to tell her we buried the kid, and plant flowers there in the spring. Plan to be gone by then.

Burned quick. Not much there, and we poured lighter fluid on the base to help it along. Held Honus while he sobbed.

Jodi is not recovering well. Can't blame her for not wanting to, right now. Dragged the kiddie pool outside, drained so much blood out of it… weird to see it all collected. Poured it out on to the snow. Still warm, and the red spread and steamed. Stared at it. Bloom bloom red the last rose. Rose red. Snow white.

She's weak, thready pulse, distraught. The two of us are tending her all day. The house is silent except that I can hear them both crying through their bedroom doors. Alone.

Each and every one of us = last person on earth.

* * * * *

Chronicles were written all over the world. Some were diaries, like the Book of the Unnamed Midwife. Others were histories of cities and settlements as the years moved by. Each marked time in their own way. Some were read, others lay forever forgotten when their owners stopped writing.

*****

The New Year went largely unmarked, except in these books. Times Square lay silent under a dusting of snow, stirred by the wind now and again. A small group in upstate New York marked the day a week later, guessing. Five men clinked glasses together in a toast to something none of them believed in anymore.

*****

On that same blistering hot day, a pair of sisters swam near the foot of Iguazu Falls on the border between Argentina and Brazil. The two of them had not seen another human being in more than a month. They stripped off their clothes and swam for hours, watching the water's surface flashing in the sun.

*****

A harem of three women in the Ukraine chose that day to kill their captor. They celebrated, but not because it was a holiday.

*****

The limited government that still functioned in Seoul appointed new guards to the facility housing the remaining two hundred and forty two women left in the country. The previous guards had been publicly shot.

*****

The winter killed many, with cold and isolation and loneliness. The Huntsville ward moved all survivors into the Bishop's large house. Bishop Graves had died of a massive heart attack, so Patty had been married to Bishop Lewis, who had been appointed on his twenty-sixth birthday.

*****

If they could have compared notes, one colony of survivors to another, they would have found that the number of successful human births on earth that year had been zero. But they did not know, and so hope persisted.

*****

Jodi had been in bed for six days when Dusty brought her Christmas presents to her.

"Hey, you don't have to get up and you don't have to talk. I wish you'd eat, but I can't make you. So I thought you might like something comforting. The batteries are all charged up."

She arranged the batteries and DVDs on the bed, and left Jodi a couple of granola bars. Jodi did not respond, even by opening her eyes. Dusty knew she was awake.

An hour later, Jodi had sat up and put her headphones on. When Honus went to check on her, she refused to look at him. The granola bars were untouched. The screen showed long-dead people dancing in a club. He kissed her on the top of her head and closed her door.

Dusty sat on the living room sofa, reading. Honus sat beside her, put his elbows on his knees, and buried his face in his hands.

"She'll come out of it," Dusty said to her book.

"She's going to die. She wants to be with the baby. She's going to leave me, too." Honus' voice was thick with tears.

Dusty was sick to death of this pain. She was awash in her own grief and terror. She thought Honus was right and Jodi would die, but it was such a small thing beside her dawning certainty that no children would ever be born again.

Never again never again look upon this wasteland.

She wanted out of her head so bad that she considered going raiding for enough alcohol to get blackout drunk and stay that way a while.

Honus' long frame sagged. His posture was all grief, and even his silence was leaden. His misery felt like a weight on her and it was all she could do to keep from screaming at him. She sat, staring into her book but not reading, deciding that she would pack up and move to another house in the neighborhood. She tried to remember which ones still held food in the pantry.

Honus pulled her book out of her hands. She looked at him and tried to conceal her anger. His eyes were enormous, red-rimmed and bright blue. He hadn't shaved in a few days. He looked for once more like a man than a boy.

"Please," he begged her.

"What?" She could barely get it out.

He crawled into her lap with an urgency that woke everything in her. Heat poured into her body from some unknown spring and she flushed all over. He clung to her like a child and she was mother and lover and barely sane.

He cried like he would break and molded himself to her. She found herself shushing him like a frightened child and laying down to hold him prone. The couch was an awkwardly small space and the two of them barely fit its width, even pressed together. He lay his face in the crook of her neck and sobbed.

She held him while a wild stabbing need ran through her body like a triangular circuit, current carried from her nipples to her clit and back again. She was out of her mind. Grief and rage and sex came together in waves of wordless ache.

She kissed him.

She kissed him and it was like a knot being untied. She tasted his tears and felt his groan in her mouth, felt him shake and harden at once.

A few gasping flurries of clothing and he was inside her without preamble. She didn't care. She was as wet as she had ever been and they ground their hips together, legs held by jeans only half rolled down. She rocked and rocked and came against him, squeezing him tight. She bit his shoulder and stifled a scream. He buried his face in her neck and whimpered as she felt him throb it out inside her. She held him as they calmed, but she could already feel him pulling away.

He rolled off the couch and knelt, fastening his pants and straightening his shirt. He glanced nervously down the hallway.

Dusty lay on her back and zipped her jeans. Done cannot be undone, and there was nothing either of them could say.

Honus walked down the hall and closed his bedroom door. Dusty did the same, and slept better and deeper than she had in months.

*January 5*

We keep saying that it can't happen again, that we shouldn't and she's going to know. But we do and I don't know if she does. We are assholes.

After the first time I wasn't sure what was going to happen, but he comes to my room most nights around midnight. Talk and fuck and talk again. Never had anyone teach him anything. Never even done it any way but missionary. Fucking a missionary. Joke funny hahaha. Loves when I show him something new but his guilt just gets deeper. Don't know what to do about it.

Jodi is not getting better. Refusing to eat. Healing slowly, not like she should. Doesn't want me looking. Won't let Honus touch her. Woke us both up screaming the other night that the baby wasn't dead but we had hidden him from her. Inconsolable = had to knock her out.

Still want to leave but the snow doesn't let up and Honus says it will break his heart. Don't know that I have a heart to break. Don't love him, just something more along the line of a need. Somewhere to pour all the things that I feel besides this book. Relief. Is that so bad? Would Jodi be angry if she knew it was only a comfort? Rationalizing. Of course she would. Betrayed. But at least I have no intention of stealing him.

Why steal men these days? Men = dime a dozen.

They always were.

* * * * *

Fuck, Jodi. I'm sorry.

The snow stopped and rain took its place. Downpour washed away the white and dripped off every edge of the house. A small leak started in the kitchen and Honus patched it with plastic as best he could. They still had to keep a pan in the place where it dripped.

Jodi came back slowly, but preferred to watch her movies all day. She didn't want to speak or eat with them. She put up with small hugs from Honus, but she would not allow Dusty to touch her. Her eyes were large with dark circles beneath and she grew thinner by the day. She did not get out of bed.

Dusty and Honus lay in her bed one night listening to the rain pattering on the roof. Some nights it was loud, like living inside a drum. Tonight it was milder, but enough that they couldn't sleep. She had fucked him four times, each time thinking he would wear out and fall asleep. He didn't.

"What's going to happen?"

"Happen to what, Honus?"

"To us. To you and me and Jodi and everybody in the world. What are we going to do?"

"I'm going to move on in the spring to somewhere I can settle down permanently. Somewhere safe with less snow and maybe where I can grow things. You two will probably go back to Huntsville, since it's what you know."

"So that's it, then?"

"What are you talking about?"

"You won't stay with me? We could be married. All three of us."

"Oh god."

"What? It's not that bad. I love you, you know."

"I know."

"That's it?"

"What do you want me to say?"

"Say that you love me too, Dusty. Jeez. I know you do. You wouldn't be with me like this if you didn't."

She stared at the ceiling. She thought about Jack, who she had loved. The way they had treated each other, how they had known each other. This was not that.

"Well?"

"You don't even know my name. Look, you love Jodi. You two can have a life together. We… all three of us, we got stuck together. If things hadn't happened this way, we probably never would have met."

"But we did meet. I believe that God sent Jodi to you for a reason."

She sighed. "Maybe I kept her from dying in childbirth. Maybe. But your reasoning sucks. God killed most of the people on Earth with a plague so that we could have all this? God sent you here to sleep with me and ruin your marriage? God set you up to burn the body of your first child?"

He didn't answer.

"Not everything has a meaning. Maybe there is no plan. Maybe there's no reason we met, and we're fucking because we were both really frustrated and lonely."

"I can't believe you think that way."

"I can't believe you still think there's a plan."

"So what if you get pregnant? We've been making love for a while, without any… protection."

She got up off the bed and grabbed her old pack. She ripped it open to show him her cache of pills and rings and patches.

"This is my plan. This is what makes sense to me. Not dying while giving birth to a dead baby. I'm going to try and give them to your wife before I leave, because without someone to attend her, she might not get through this again. So there is no 'what if.' Don't worry about it. What you need to worry about is that your wife may be the only woman in the county or in the state after I leave. That should worry you."

"What do you think will happen? Someone will—"

"Kill you. Rape her. Maybe make you watch. Maybe you'll go back to Huntsville and you'll have an accident so that someone else can marry her. I've seen what it's like out there. As long as you've got her, you've got trouble."

"Then you're in just as much danger. Why not stay and let me—"

"Let you protect me. While your wife hates my guts because I let her baby die and then fucked her husband. That sounds grand, when do we start?"

"Why are you being like this?"

"I don't belong here. I can't stay. Just please let this be what it is. Don't try to make it last forever."

They lay and the sound of the rain talked over them.

"What is your real name?"

"What did you name the baby?"

Honus got up and left.

*January 10*

Want to leave in the middle of the night without a word. Don't owe anything. Not even an explanation. Want to run the fuck away from all of this. From everything. Toward nothing. Where do I go? For what, to who? Honus isn't an answer, this doesn't fix anything. Honus = placebo.

Grow carrots. Eat carrots. Shit carrots. Die. That's the best thing I can imagine. And the last generation of humanity winds down to zero. Got into the wrong business after graduation. Profession is doomed.

Can't leave without a word. Can't leave them raw like Roxanne left me. Can't be a mystery like Jack is a mystery. Make them hate me, or leave with grace. Hate is easier.

Get her to take the shot. Give her enough to share. Tell her not to give it to that Patty kid until menarche. Not sure she can handle it, or will do it at all. Have to try. Prolong life preserve quality of life fight for life FOR WHAT FOR WHAT FOR WHAT

If I do it now, there won't be any snow to show it. Get away from the house, let the rain wash me away. They'd never find me. Leave without my pack and they'll know. Leave with only the gun and they'll know. Do it with a needle and they might not know. No. No. No.

Not gonna do it. Can't come up with a good reason except the awful fucking awful way I feel, but not gonna do it. Fuck a reason why. There never was a reason why. Making copies is not a reason why. Now until the end is mine, and I won't spend it in misery/ boredom/terror.

Gonna leave. Soon. But won't punish them with it. Don't deserve that.

* * * * *

Dusty woke up in the morning and the two of them were crying in Jodi's room together. She walked to the door. It was open, but she stood in the doorway without entering.

They sat together on Jodi's bed, sobbing. It took them a while to notice her. Honus stood up when he did, rubbing his hands on the legs of his pants.

"She had a nightmare."

Dusty nodded. Jodi looked like she'd been crying all night, but she looked alive. Alert.

"Do you want to try and eat something?"

Jodi nodded, but she did not look up.

Dusty walked away to the kitchen. She was planning to carry the plates back to the bedroom but Jodi and Honus came quietly to the kitchen table. Dusty made them powdered milk to drink and sat down with her solitary cup of coffee, eyeing them both with a weary dread.

Jodi drank milk and ate a forkful of egg. Honus cleaned his plate as always.

"So, did you decide to live?"

Jodi looked up. "What?"

Dusty was not in the mood to talk at the speed she normally set for conversations with Jodi.

"Did you decide to live instead of dying slowly in that bed? Are you going to live, or are you just going to have breakfast before you die?"

"It's not like a decision. I'm just alive. I didn't decide anything."

"Bullshit." She drank her coffee.

Stubbornly, Jodi ate another forkful of egg.

Honus cleared his throat and pushed his plate away. "Jodi… we both think we should go back to Huntsville. Not now, when she's stronger. I'm going to look around for a car, but we might end up having to walk.

Dusty nodded. It was what she predicted they'd do.

"You could come with us…" Honus looked at Dusty and she couldn't look away.

"Go on."

"You'd be welcome in Huntsville. You'd…we'd have to tell them… You couldn't fool them forever."

"Mhmm. And then I entertain suitors."

"The bishop would…"

Dusty started to laugh. "Show me where to get my white dress. I can't wait."

"What are you going to do, Dusty? Where are you going to go?"

"Not Huntsville." She sipped her coffee.

"Can't you just…" Honus was not crying yet, but she could see it coming.

I can't and you can't. Jodi needs you and I don't. Get the hint, Honus.

"I had a nightmare." Jodi was staring at the middle of the table, at nothing. "I had a nightmare about the two of you. Honus was cheating on me with you. Isn't that weird?"

"That's really weird, Jodi. Why do you think you dreamt that?"

Honus' face had lost all its color. He sat rigidly in place and did not speak.

"I guess I had been thinking about the baby for so long—" Her voice caught on the word 'baby,' but she pushed through it. "That I forgot I have a husband. And I love him, and he needs my attention. You know?"

"Yes, that makes sense." She was cold. Completely cold, in her veins and in her heart there was nothing but cold, cold water.

"Like, I know it would never really happen because you're gay and stuff."

"Am I now?"

Jodi ignored her. "But still, I woke up really mad. Like really mad. So I woke up Honus and told him we had to move on. Try again."

"Try again?"

"Once I've healed. We can try again to have a baby."

"I see." Dusty drained her coffee cup. "I have a counter-offer. I have drugs that will help you—"

"No. I'm not going to take birth control in this world. This world needs babies more than it needs anything else."

"I can give it to you. In case you change your mind."

"I'm not going to. I'm sure that Honus and I will have a baby that will live. I don't want it."

"You might change your mind if you live through another one like this."

Jodi's eyes reddened. "That won't happen again."

"No. You're right. Next time, without any help, you'll probably die. Duty done, punch out. I tried to have babies who would die but instead I did the dying myself. Hang a wreath around me, call me saint. Call me mama."

Jodi got up so suddenly that her chair shot out behind her. "You're just jealous! You're just jealous of me and Honus because you have nobody!"

I could tell her now and it would destroy them both. Take the last thing I know that hasn't fallen apart and crumble it. For what?

Dusty did not move. She stared into her empty coffee cup. "If only I had my own sexless marriage and dead baby. Then I could be like you. You're right. You have so much and I wish, Jodi. I wish."

"Dusty." Honus spoke to her as though punishment was his to give.

Dad's mad. Fuck you.

"Fuck you both," she said rising from the table. "Go when you want. I am done giving a shit. Don't worry about your nightmare, Jodi. Your husband is as uninterested in sex as you are. Save it for procreation. He doesn't care."

She walked out of the room and went to the back of the house. She started to pack.

* * * * *

The house was silent. Dusty dreamed of Roxanne, who spoke in Jack's voice. "Hey, sweets. Let's walk the bridge?"

"Where are we going?"

"With the chicken."

She turned around and saw they were on the Golden Gate Bridge, and Chicken was there, holding Joe's hand.

"To get to the other side," he said sullenly.

* * * * *

Jodi dreamed of her baby boy. If she sat him down, she could watch him and see him smile. He made sweet little gurgling noise and she ached all over. When she picked him up, she was only holding a twisted-up blanket. She woke up alone in her bed and cried softly until she drifted back out to sleep.

* * * * *

Honus dreamed that he was with Jodi, but Jodi wanted him with the heat and abandon that Dusty had shown. Her belly was round and tight between them and he knew that the child would be a girl.

"We'll have to sell her." Jodi was Dusty, her face changed and her voice was no one's. Her lips didn't move. "If we sell her she'll be safe."

"We can't do that."

"We can do it in Mexico." Jodi was naked, but out of reach. Receding. Receding. Out of reach.

* * * * *

Somehow the three of them knew that today would be the day. At first light they were all up and making ready.

Jodi found Dusty in the pantry.

"Hey, I was going to pack up most of this, since you guys are headed to Huntsville. But if there's anything you want, you can have it."

"You hate powdered eggs anyways."

Dusty did not turn to face her. "I do. You can definitely have those. The Ovaltine, too."

"Hey. Dusty?"

She turned this time.

"Nevermind." Jodi left the kitchen.

I never did.

Dusty walked back to her room and passed Honus in the hallway. He was carrying a bag out to the front porch. It looked as though the Obermeyers were packing light.

Dusty grabbed a rifle and a box of shells and followed him out.

"Take this."

"I don't need it."

"You don't know what you'll need. Maybe you'll hunt with it."

He took it uncertainly and gently set the butt of it down on the ground. "I don't know how to use it."

"Jodi does. I taught her the basics. Just take it, ok?"

"Ok."

She stalked back in. When she came into the living room, she was ready to go. She was carrying more than she wanted to and she knew she would not go far today.

Honus had his hand on Jodi's shoulder. "Go ahead."

Jodi looked sullen. "I… should thank you. You probably did save my life. Thank you. Like really, thank you."

Dusty looked from Jodi to Honus. "You don't have to thank me. It's just what I do. You also don't have to do anything Honus tells you. Not now, not ever. He needs you way more than you need him. Think about that."

She turned to him, suddenly. "Could you leave us alone for a minute? Just step out on the porch. One sec." She turned back to Jodi without waiting for an answer. Dismissed by Dusty's eyes, Honus stepped out.

She pulled a brick of plastic cartridges out of her bag. "This is enough birth control for three years. You just take one a day. It's very simple."

Jodi did not reach for the banded bundle. "I told you, I'm not going to-"

"Listen, listen. Just listen to me for one second and then you won't ever have to do it again. Something bad is going to happen. I guarantee it will. Probably it's going to happen to Honus, and you're going to have to deal with a lot of guys. Maybe they'll be ok, maybe they won't."

"It won't! You don't know."

Dusty glared. "Fine then, I'm crazy and nothing has changed and you'll be in charge of bake sales forever. In case you're not, hide these somewhere. And if you end up with someone who isn't Honus, maybe who isn't a nice person, you have the option to not go through this again. Or maybe if you and Honus are unlucky again, you'll want to take a year or two off from this horror. Or give it to Patty when she gets her blood. Just fucking take them. Take them. Just to remind yourself that you have the option. Ok?"

Jodi accepted them finally, and when she looked up Dusty could see she was crying. "You don't understand. It isn't going to be like that. Everything's going to be…" Jodi lost her breath, strangling to hold in sobs.

"Wonderful. Everything is wonderful. Be careful, Jodi. Keep your eyes open." The impulse to hug her was strong, despite everything. She was tired of them, but still it tore a little.

Honus came back in and Jodi went out. She did not say goodbye.

As soon as the door closed, Honus took Dusty in his arms. He crushed her to him and she was turned on, all the way up, instantly ready. He kissed her and she shook. She pulled back from him, disgust beginning to well up within her.

"Come with us. Please come with us. Don't let it end like this. We'll work it out."

"Honus, don't embarrass yourself. We're done here."

His face went white.

"Look, you're a coward. You'll never really be honest with

Jodi, not about you or me or anything else. You don't know how. I think you married her so that you'd never have to try too hard."

"That's not why."

"Shhh. Almost done. What I told you will happen, about someone trying to take her from you, that's going to happen. That will happen soon. Watch your back, don't go on any mysterious errands or hunting trips. Don't trust anyone. Remember that you have the one thing that everyone wants."

He was shaking his head, grinning. "I knew you loved me. I knew it. You wouldn't be so worried if you didn't."

"That's not why."

"Why, then? Why do you even care?" He smiled like a man who knows he has won.

"Because you're both helpless. This is like helping a kitten get out of a tree. It's not love, it's pity. Just try to stay alive, ok?"

Smile gone, he reached out to take her hand. She had cut her hair down to nothing and bound and bundled. She shifted her pack on to her shoulders and ignored his gesture.

"Come on, Dusty. Come on."

She looked back to him and put her hand out. He held it awkwardly and they stared at one another.

After a moment, he let go. She adjusted her pack and headed to the door. The house seemed dingy with their shared life. Outside of it, she felt the twin dawning of loneliness and relief.

"You know where we'll be." Honus raised his hand in farewell.

"I know. Goodbye." She turned her back and started to walk. They watched her a minute before turning to head to Huntsville.

* * * * *

The Obermeyers were welcomed warmly at the stake center. Nothing was made of their absence and they were not asked to explain it. Less than a dozen in Huntsville had survived. Jodi was the third woman. The ratio of men to women was closer, but competition had increased. Close living quarters and desperation had made the congregation touchy and ragged.

Bishop Lewis was jealous of Patty to the point that no one saw her. She was as closeted as she had ever been, and spent her days sewing and mending for the household. Sister Sterling told Jodi first when the day came that following summer that Patty had gotten her first period. Jodi's thoughts ran to the untouched brick of pills Dusty had given her, but she said nothing.

Jodi miscarried twice that year. Both times it was early, and she had told no one. She put them out of mind as hard late periods. Not children. Just blood. Just cramps and a few tired days.

Two more suicides slipped out in the night. Bishop Lewis was furious and began setting a night watch so that no one could get away from the house they all shared. The house was old, built more than a hundred years before. Young men were bunked together in twos and threes in the old servants' quarters. Jodi and Honus had a small room to themselves close to the master suite.

They were the first to know when Lewis started having sex

with Patty. The crying went on and on, even when the shrieking had stopped.

The night watches failed and little by little people dispersed. Two young men one night and three the next. The weather was warming up and they were close to other small towns where they knew they could settle.

By August, the three couples remained. The Sterlings were badly matched and hardly spoke to one another. Lewis and the hollow-eyed Patty behaved around each other as predator and prey. Jodi and Honus grew insular, spending all their time together, trying to live inside a bubble that kept out the rest of the world.

Sister Sterling was gone one day and her husband raged after her in a car, determined to bring her back. Neither one returned. In the fall, Honus asked Jodi to leave with him.

Jodi had a moment alone with Patty. She gave the girl a laundry basket full of clothes she told her needed mending. They were old clothes she didn't want anymore.

Inside them was the entire three year supply.

Honus and Jodi opened the front door and walked out that night as the full moon rose. Without a word, they walked back to the house where they had spent the last winter. It was exactly the way they had left it. They set about provisioning the house for the winter.

Honus searched and searched for a sign of Dusty, for anything she had left behind. He had a wild hope that he would find a note from her like he had once found from his wife. Unidentifiable hairs in the shower drain, anonymous finger smudges on the doorframe. Books she must have touched but had left no trace. He and Jodi slept together in the room that had once been only hers. He sat in Dusty's room sometimes, to think. He pulled open her dresser drawers one day and found neatly folded in the top drawer the pajamas he had given her for Christmas. He touched them gently and closed the drawer.

The Obermeyers celebrated Christmas again that year, but it felt hollow. Honus brought his wife more DVDs and batteries, she surprised him with a very nice pocketknife. They sang the same songs and lit the same tree. They both felt like hell, and they talked long into the night.

"It's not right. It wasn't enough. We shouldn't have left her there."

"What wasn't enough?" Honus didn't understand.

"Never mind. We have to go get her. We have to."

"You're right. I'm scared to do it, but you're right."

They went out and started up the snowmobile. They rode back into Huntsville and let themselves in the unlocked door of the house. It was silent and dark. They crept up the stairs. Patty and Lewis were in a king bed, feet of distance between them. The girl slept curled tight into a ball. Jodi held the rifle and aimed it at Lewis. Honus woke Patty up quietly. She opened her eyes wide at his first touch. She scrambled out of bed naked and stood blue-white in the starlight that came through the window.

"Who's there?" Lewis was awake and peering into the dark.

"It's Jodi and Honus Obermeyer. We're taking Patty to live with us." Jodi sounded surer than she felt. She had her finger on the rifle's trigger, but she had forgotten to load it.

"You can't take my wife." Lewis was struggling up out of bed. He was a young man, but he was working on an impressive beard already. He wore white shorts and had to feel on the nightstand for his glasses.

Honus had found a nightgown and dropped it over Patty's head. She raised her arms obediently, letting him dress her like a doll. "Do you want to stay here?"

Patty couldn't answer. Her eyes were pure terror.

"See, she's fine. Now you two go on back to wherever you came from." He stared at the barrel of the rifle while he spoke.

Honus picked Patty up off her feet. She weighed nothing at all. He held her to his chest and she was rigid, trembling.

Honus walked out the bedroom door and Jodi inched backwards to follow.

"Who do you think you are? You can't just come in here and—"

"She's just a kid! What you're doing is wrong and you know it."

"She's a woman, and she's my wife. When she's older she'll understand better. It's just hard for her to understand right now."

Jodi was still moving backwards. "Don't follow us or I'll shoot. Stay right here." She turned and slammed the door behind her. She bolted down the stairs to the snowmobile where Honus had Patty on the seat behind him and Jodi got on after so that the two of them held her there.

As they pulled away, they saw Lewis come out the front door yelling, waving his arms at them. Honus prayed that he didn't have a gun. There was no sound of a shot.

They made it home and got Patty dressed and drinking hot Ovaltine in front of the tree. It took Lewis hours to follow their tracks back to Eden. He rattled the doorknob, screaming.

Honus took the rifle and loaded it. "Go to the back of the house." Jodi took Patty to the back bedroom and the two of them sat in the closet. Honus opened the door.

"She's staying with us, and you're going to leave." He held the rifle low, but kept it pointed toward Lewis.

Lewis was shivering. His cheeks were red and his glasses were fogged. "Don't be ridiculous. I am your bishop and she is my wife."

"You're not our bishop anymore. We—" The gun went off as his nervous hand squeezed it. The shot hit Lewis in his hip and he went down, wheezing. Honus dropped the gun in shock and stared. Jodi ran out to them.

"Oh my gosh. You shot him!"

Honus could only stare.

"What do we do?"

He shook his head and his jaw worked, but no sound came out.

"Shoot him again." It was Patty. They both turned to look.

Patty stood there as if she had not spoken.

"I can't. I can't." Honus was approaching hysteria. He was gasping tiny breaths, his chest hitching.

Patty picked up the gun and looked at it. It was nearly as tall as she was, and she had never handled one before. Gently, Jodi took it from her. She worked the bolt and took a deep breath. She aimed at Lewis' head and pulled the trigger. The hole was small but blood gushed out, staining the snow.

Honus sat down hard and his eyelashes fluttered. He grayed out.

Jodi put the rifle beside the door and pushed Patty back inside. Then she helped Honus to stumble to the couch. She locked the door.

"We're gonna be a family. No one is ever going to mess with us, like ever again." She sat down next to Honus and patted his hand. He did not respond.

Patty was cold, but present. She pulled her knees up under her chin.

Jodi started a song and Patty joined her. Honus took more than an hour to come back to himself.

In the morning, Jodi told him to bury the body. He built a pyre as Dusty had once done and burned it. He came back to the house and found Jodi and Patty talking like sisters.

The three of them got on very well. They were a family, as Jodi had said. They never spoke of Lewis and they rarely spoke of the plague or the time before. Jodi miscarried over and over, and she told Patty what had happened with their first child. Patty listened without emotion. She said she would never get married again.

* * * * *

Six years later, Jodi went full term with a girl. They both died, the child never left her body. Honus was wrecked with grief and Patty did the burning. Four bodies, one place. The rain churned their ashes into the soil.

* * * * *

It was less than a year before the two of them started sleeping together. Patty was barren. They lived together the rest of their lives and never again saw another human being.

## Chapter Eleven

The boys worked short days. They came in after breakfast and worked patiently, diligently until midday. They shared lunch at long tables in the old cafeteria. The room was windowless, with a stage at one end. They had decorated the walls with their drawings and calligraphy, many of them were developing a neat hand. When they had eaten, they had a few hours to play and run their energy off. Some of them napped in the late afternoon, others spent time in the library.

The library had been painstakingly collected and was maintained by people who cared for books beyond all things. No books could leave that building; reading could only be done there. Couches and cushions and chairs were scattered throughout and usually occupied. The scribe boys favored the books that explained parts of the before time, books that were everyday stories of peoples' lives. Their studies focused on farming and writing and the repair of simple machines, but left to their own devices the boys read books about small families and big cities and the way things used to be.

The boys did not live in families. They were part of large co-op households to which they had been given when they were weaned. They had never seen a big city. The big cities of the world crumbled and fell overtaken by rats and ivy, undermined by floods and rust.

For a year of their lives, they reported for five days to copy the Books in their neat and even hands. They were eager to please. Their letters were perfect, their lines were straight. They smiled up at Mother Ina who tousled their hair and told them they were good. When they neared the end of the year, they asked her what they would do next.

"Soon it will be time to choose apprenticeships. You'll meet people in the trades and see what interests you. Soon enough. But today, we return to this. Are you boys ready?"

They were ready. Hands clean, paper laid out, ink wells full.

THE BOOK OF THE UNNAMED MIDWIFE
THE HIVE of VIVIAN

*March 21*

Farmhouse on the 80. More corn than I thought there'd be. Weird corn. Different colors, mixed colors. Cross pollinating. Corn – farmers + wind. Delicious. Roast it and don't think about butter. Thirteen days since I saw another person. Distance. No idea who they were. Didn't care. Didn't see me.

Not the last man on earth. Even if I never saw anyone I'd know because fucking food is disappearing. Deer in the corn. Day will come. No more sardines no more tuna no more pb or j. Need to get more rural. Same as it ever was and everybody goes to Walmart. Better odds in podunk little two by four kind of places. Restaurant kitchens. Sit in an old vinyl booth and casually remark that I'll have the fried chicken. Right. Tell it to the millipedes for they have inherited the earth.

Also can't find a fucking god damned water filter anywhere of any kind. Boiling everything. Fucking tiresome. Tastes bad.

*March 30*

Swear to shit, flocks of wild chickens. Shot two. Plucking is bullshit but remember Christmas dinner. Ate the both of them roasted and burning my fingers. Sprinkled with salt packets from a McDonalds. Hope they breed. Hope the world is covered in wild chickens.

People nearby. Feel it.

*April 1*

No fools. Vivian and fourteen men. Wearing furs. Welcomed me like it was time for cake at Versailles. Well-provisioned. Pretended like I had no skills. She bought the drag. Dirty, haven't bathed in ages. Said nothing about my guns, totally peaceable. Not one of them made a move without her say. Never seen anything like it.

Alpha and a handful of betas. Biggest dude = predictably alpha, but after that pretty random. Betas who sing and fix things and one ugly little funny guy. Rest come and go but loyal. Invited me to dinner and a long group fuck. Didn't join but watched. Amazing. Laughing the whole time. She got off more times than I could count, gave them almost nothing. Threw them out if they came too fast or couldn't take direction. Arrogant. Plain looking, but so confident = sexy.

Before I left asked if she needed BC. Laughed and told me she was covered if she lived to be a thousand. She might.

*April 25*

Passed by a person on horseback for the first time in my life. No idea male or female. Wearing a cape. Wtf.

*April 26*

Coming into Des Moines. Not sure if I'm going to avoid the city or not. Obviously inhabited. Fires.

*April 29*

Long sign with streamers made of shreds of cloth. TOP PRICE PAID FOR FEMALE ANY AGE DURABLE GOODS MEDICINE GUNS CITY HALL AT SUNDOWN EVERY DAY

Cutting around Des Moines.

* * * * *

The woods were deep green and dripped with rain. Mushrooms carpeted the ground and trails were wiped out with new growth. She stomped through heavily, headed for a house she had glimpsed through the trees. She had headed due south out of Des Moines. She knew she was in Missouri, but not where.

The house was small and it had once been white. Moss grew up one side and reached around the face of it, green fingers slipping toward the windows. She found the door locked so she kicked it in. The wood was swollen and wet and gave way with a rotted creak. She hurried in and dropped her pack, glad to be out of the wet woods.

There was dry firewood inside and she started a fire. The pantry was bare. She dug out her last can of chicken soup and heated it. She would eat it slowly.

She hadn't made a sound in more than a month, other than moaning in her sleep. She wasn't sure she could talk if she wanted to. Her voice was something that fell away, unneeded. Vestigial vocal cords. She hadn't fired her guns in a long time. She wiped them down with oil, made sure they were dry and in order before putting them back together and settling in to sleep. She laid out her wet clothes to dry and sat in front of the fire in just her binder and panties, warming her back and then her front. When she felt as dry and warm as she could get, she pulled clothes out of her pack. They weren't dry either, so she laid them out.

She dragged a couch in front of the fireplace so that the arms of it touched the brick pediment. She curled up on it and slept.

She awoke the second the door opened. She pulled both guns out from under the cushion where they'd been wedged and waiting, holding her breath.

"What the hell? Who started a fire in here?" The room filled with the light of several lanterns.

"Hello?"

The first voice was a man's, but the second was not. Cautiously, she peeked up over the back of the couch.

"Oh shit." The woman dropped her lantern. It stayed lit as it rolled across the floor. Shadows spun.

"Who the hell are you?" The man was short, with thick black chest hair showing over the open buttons of his soggy flannel. His face was covered in a stubbly beard and he looked as if he had fallen in mud.

She held both guns where they couldn't be seen. "Just a traveler." She tried to speak low but her unused voice squeaked and gave her away. She was either a woman or a boy going through puberty. She cleared her throat and started again. "Just a—"

The man stepped forward quickly, his face showing pure shock. "You're a woman!"

She raised both guns over the back of the couch and rested them there. "Stop. Not another step."

"Whoa, hey. Hang on there." The other woman stooped to pick up her blue electric lantern and stepped between them. In the firelight, she too was covered in mud. She wiped her face a little. Her skin was the color of dark honey and her hair was pulled back but the curls showed through. Her large black eyes took in the woman on the couch and her guns and did not flinch. She radiated calm, absolutely unruffled.

"Hey, I'm Ava and this is Dino. We're ok, we're not here to hurt you. This place is a way station that we use sometimes. We're on our way back from a shopping trip. We're armed too, but I'd rather see you put yours away then get mine out." She was smiling just a little.

The midwife stared at her. She was deciding.

"I want to put my clothes on. I'm gonna put my guns down and do that, and then we can talk." She stared at Dino. He showed her his hands and then turned his back.

"Please, go ahead and get dressed. I'll give you some privacy."

She knelt awkwardly and pushed the couch back from the hearth. Her jeans were toasty as she put them on. The zipper was too hot to touch. She left it open and shrugged back into her long underwear. It fit her tight and made things clear, but they already knew. She put the guns back in her waistband and zipped up. She walked out to face Ava.

"Alright. Guns away."

"That's great. So, what's your name?"

She closed her lips for a second.

Nope.

"Jane."

"Jane." Ava held out her hand. The custom already felt ancient. They shook.

Dino came back around and offered his, too. "Dino. It's really Dean, but everyone calls me Dino." He shook vigorously and smiled at her. "Where you headed?"

"East. North. Maybe New England."

The two exchanged a glance. "What are you looking for?"

"A safe place."

"With other people?" Dino was looking up at her from under raised brows.

"Are other people safe?"

Ava spoke this time. "Some people are. Look, we were driving a truck full of supplies through the wood when we got stuck in the mud. We've got plenty to eat. We both need to clean up, but we were going to have a late supper. Want to join us and maybe talk a little?"

Jane had eaten, but she wasn't going to turn down a little more. "Okay. We can talk."

Dino heated two pots of water from a cistern and bathed methodically in the kitchen sink. When he was done he rinsed it out and put water on to boil for Ava.

"Thank you." She pulled her muddy shirt off and dropped it in a heap on the floor. She followed it with her stretchy pants. "We've got new clothes, Dino. Let's ditch these."

Jane watched Dino very carefully while Ava undressed. He looked, but it was incidental. She saw no hunger there. While Ava bathed, Dino heated up cans of beef stew and set out a can of peaches. "For dessert," he said with a little smile. Jane was still watching.

She sat down in one of the chairs at the small dining table. When they joined her, she felt she sat with Honus and Jodi again.

"So where did you come from?"

"San Francisco. Spent a winter in Utah. Traveling, mostly."

"Have you seen many people?" Ava was eating hungrily, but Dino seemed eager to talk.

"A few."

"Mostly men?"

"Yeah, mostly men. Where did you come from?"

"I'm from St. Louis. When the city got bad, I got out."

Ava swallowed and reached for her water glass. "I'm from Texas. Came through hell to get here. I've seen things you wouldn't believe."

Jane managed half a smile. "I might."

"So things are the same on the west coast?" Dino did not seem disappointed. He was like a man patting the stump of a lost limb. Just checking.

"Same all over. Dead and dying."

Ava fell back into her stew.

"So I noticed your tattoo." Dino nodded to Jane's chest where the black figure of a caduceus was inked.

Her hand went to it. She had caught Honus staring at it but he had never asked. It had been a long time since she looked at it, really thought about it.

"Yeah?"

"Yeah, are you a doctor?"

"I'm a midwife."

The word hung there a minute.

"I might be the last midwife on Earth."

"Well," Ava gulped again. "You might be, but at least you've got medical training. That's a great skill." She applied herself to licking the bowl.

"Yeah I'm trained as a nurse. Not just babies. Great because babies are about out of business."

Ava and Dino shared another glance. Jane decided she could wait it out.

"Do either of you need medical attention?" Her cool professional eye was on them. They didn't.

"I know a man who died of tetanus this year. We think it was tetanus. He got cut on some tiny thing, like a rusty nail. We didn't know what to do. We could use somebody…" He looked at Ava. Ava sighed.

"We have a place," Ava said carefully. "It's very safe. Enclosed. Defensible. We're not really looking to take in new people, but we never turn down women or girls. Combine that with your training, and of course we want you."

Jane was stiff. She waited.

"We're not going to make you. Nobody will lay a hand on you. Believe me, I know how this sounds. I got sold twice before I got out of Texas. I lost my daughter out there." Her eyes were wet but nothing fell.

"Sold?"

"Once for guns and once for penicillin. Both times to gangs of guys. The first gang killed my daughter, she was thirteen."

Ava dropped her chin to her shoulder, as if she were looking behind her. She took a few breaths. No one spoke. She started again when she was steady.

"Second time, the gang of guys fell apart, starting killing each other. I end up with this asshole, Eddie. Eddie sold me for penicillin after he got pneumonia. He shot the guy he sold me to and took me back. The penicillin killed him. I took his gun and his car and ran."

"Allergic."

"Yeah, that's what I think, too." Ava's eyes were intelligent and steely. Jane adjusted her opinion of the woman and listened closely.

"You didn't get pregnant?"

"IUD."

"Good for you."

"Good old Planned Parenthood. Saved my life."

They shared a moment, a knowing. Dino did not intrude.

"What about you?"

Jane looked at her steadily. "I got into trouble a couple of times. Killed some men. Never got captured. Or sold."

Fuck, am I bragging? Hope she doesn't think I feel superior. Only luck.

"Good for you."

"Do you want to come with us? If you don't like it, you can take off anytime. We don't hold people." Dino looked hopeful. He finished his stew and kept his eyes down. He was studiedly trying not to look eager. He had learned to mask the intensity of his feelings toward women, Jane could see it. He was consciously trying not scare her, and she liked him for it.

Jane thought about it. She spooned up the last of her stew. "I'll go with you. I want to see it, at least."

In the morning, they walked out to the truck and packed sticks under the stuck wheels to get it out. They piled into the cab and drove.

Fifty miles away, they came to the gates of a military fort. The sign had been covered over. Jane couldn't read what had been underneath, it just looked like bumps under the paint. The hand-painted top layer read "Fort Nowhere."

*June 16*

Fort Nowhere = 124 men 17 women 6 boys 2 girls. Cohesive. Peaceful.

Only a handful of military left. One guy who was here when medevac brought people in. Slowly seeing everybody for check-ups. Place has a real infirmary, equipped for basic hospital functions. Sterile instruments. Slip right back in. Even wearing scrubs.

Two pregnant women, all but four of the others now on BC. One girl near menarche, the other has a few years yet.

One case of hepatitis. Couple of skin infections, one poorly healed knife wound. No STIs in the population = miracle. Basic care and all grateful, all relieved to see me.

Pros of staying: decent people. Met a few I can talk to, even some funny guys. Bernardo, Isaac. Couple of women I really like. Rachel. Callie. Place is clean, organized. Well stocked but they're setting up gardens for next spring. Nobody has gotten into my space at all.

Council of five in charge, but everyone votes. The vote on punishments was unanimous. That was a shock but it's a pro. Some large arrangements, some monogamy. Three single women not including me. Dating, fucking for sure. But no coercion. Handful of men sleeping together. Convenience. Attraction. Adjustment.

Cons of staying: no other medicos, going to get worked to death if people get sick. Can't let them become dependent. Train my replacement. Won't keep me, can walk right out the door anytime. Might as well stay. Free to stay = free to go.

# Chapter Twelve

When Jane had been at Fort Nowhere for a few months, strangers approached the gates. Two men and a handcuffed girl, a teenager. Her face was covered and the handcuffs were rusted in their joints.

The men asked about trade but found that the fort was not open to trading guns. They pulled back the girl's hood and offered her in exchange for letting them stay. The night guard let them in.

Bernardo was one of the guards. He was tall and muscular, good with a bow. Very handsome. When he knocked at Jane's door, she was happy to find him there. He told her why he needed her and her smile faded.

"Bring the girl to the infirmary alone. Wake the council to meet with the men."

Jane's living quarters were nearest to the infirmary. They had moved someone else out so that she could be there. She was in her scrubs and walking through the doors in less than five minutes.

The girl sat on the exam table listlessly. She was milk-pale, once her face was uncovered. Jane could see the blue veins in her arms from across the room. The girl's hair was coal black and her eyes seemed the same. She stared.

Jane spoke gently. "Are you alright?"

She shook her head.

"Are you hurt? Are you pregnant?"

The girl shrugged.

"What's your name?"

She whispered and her voice was tiny. Up close she was a big girl, maybe nineteen or twenty.

"Colleen."

"Hi Colleen. I'm Jane. I'm here to help you, ok?"

She nodded.

"I want to check you out to make sure you're alright. I don't want to do anything that will hurt you or scare you, but I need to look at your body. Is that alright?"

Colleen nodded and teared up. She stood up and stripped quickly, efficiently.

Her eyes were red-rimmed and her lips pressed together. She sat back down. She was gone from her body. She looked at nothing.

Jane looked over the bruises and scrapes, the ligature marks at her wrists and knew the story. She palpated the girl's belly and determined that she was not pregnant. Wonder of wonders.

Colleen's inner thighs were bruised and she showed handprints and finger marks all over. When Jane probed gingerly at the girl's vulva, she got a shock.

"Who did this to you?"

Colleen shrugged, not looking.

"It was a while ago. More than a year, right? Maybe two?"

She nodded.

"Was it the guys you're with now?"

She shook her head.

"But these two raped you. Recently. Probably today."

"Every day." The same baby voice.

Jane gave her back her clothes. She wanted to hug her, to hold her hand but she thought the girl had had enough. She looked out the door to where Bernardo had posted guard for her. She told him to go get Old Maria. The old woman was always perfectly calm, and would care for anyone.

"Please tell Maria to give her a good dinner and put her in her spare bed. This girl shouldn't be alone."

Bernardo nodded and was off. Jane waited until Old Maria came.

"Colleen, would you like to go with Old Maria? She's got dinner and a nice warm bed for you. Is that alright?"

The girl nodded again.

"Listen, you're not going back with those guys. Nobody is going to hurt you here. Nobody will even touch you unless you say ok. I promise that. Ok?"

Colleen did not look as though she believed Jane or cared. She went where she was told. Jane went to the council room.

Council was set up in the offices that had formerly belonged to the fort's commanding officer. Only Daniel had been summoned to meet with the traders. Female members of council were not called upon to deal with outsiders.

The two men were kept standing. They wore ragged ponchos and stank of unwashed bodies. When Jane walked into the room, they started.

"Holy shit."

"Where's Colleen?"

Jane ignored them and spoke to Daniel. Daniel was in his fifties. A career military man, his bearing was erect and his clothes looked pressed every time she saw him. He took to leadership naturally, but without the insecurity that drives a man to be cruel.

"Daniel, Colleen is badly injured. Her genitals were cut a few years ago by someone with a dull knife and no brains. These two are rapists."

Daniel nodded curtly. He had expected that the men would be of no use, but genital cutting was something new.

"Hey, we didn't cut up her pussy. She was like that when we bought her. Some old guy did that."

"But you have been forcing her to have sex with both of you?" Daniel's eyes were ice.

"Well, she belongs to us. We care for her and feed her. It's an arrangement." The two men were bearded twins with the same shiftless way of talking. Jane could not tell them apart.

"Do you two have anything else to say?"

"You're not gonna let us stay, are you? We'll just take our girl and be on our way."

"Do you mind if I do it, Daniel?"

Daniel sighed. "No, but don't do it in here. I'll send for a burial detail. Take them to the field."

Jane pulled her revolver out of the back of her scrubs and pointed it at the last man who had spoken.

"Turn around and walk out the door."

The other man reached under his poncho and pulled his gun. Jane shot him in the eye from a distance of three feet and he crumpled.

"Sorry, Daniel."

"Shit. Get him out of here." Daniel touched his ears, frowning.

Jane pointed her gun at the other one. "Move."

He did.

They walked out together to the spot they called Potter's Field.

He was talking fast. "Look, I'm a mechanic. I can fix things. You wouldn't be sorry if you kept me. There's no reason to get all bent out of shape about Colleen. She's fine. It wasn't a big deal, she just wasn't that into it. But she—"

"I'm only walking you out here to keep you from becoming a carpet stain. Shut up."

"Oh so you just take her side of it? Is that all?"

"Did you fuck her today?"

"Well yeah."

"Did she say yes?"

"You don't understand."

"Stand or kneel?"

"Please don't shoot. Please. I'll make it up to her. I'll never touch her again, or anyone else. I didn't mean to hurt her." His eyes were green in his haggard face. They darted as he begged.

"I can't fix you. I don't have the time to teach you why you're wrong if you don't already know. So this is it. Stand or kneel?"

He lunged toward her. She took the shot and he pitched forward, laid out on the ground.

The burial detail arrived as Jane was walking away. "Check him, he might have a good knife for one of you."

Jane got out of her scrubs and into bed. She slept with her door unlocked. She dreamed of nothing at all.

* * * * *

When the settlement at Fort Nowhere had been in place for seven years, Jane was nominated to council. It was only a gesture. She could not leave her work. But the people of the fort trusted her, they knew how she decided and how she acted. She saw them through seven hard winters with minimal loss of life. She treated the flu and kept panic about fever to a minimum. She delivered dead babies and buried mothers. She established the hospice and trained attendants so that when Old Maria began to show the signs of cancer there was a network in place to see her mercifully to her death.

Refugees and wanderers came. Some could stay, some could not. No one with medical training joined the community, so Jane began training a couple of sharp teenagers. Every once in a while, the Council debated creating a school, but the population did not grow. They did not see the point.

Jane's diaries gained legendary status even as she wrote them. The books were always in evidence in the infirmary. When her time was most scarce, she would ask others to add to the story of where they came from and what they had seen. Not everyone took her up on it, but still the story grew. When she ran out of space in the journal she had, an order was given to a raiding crew to bring back more. The crew returned with a trunk full. Journaling caught on as a fad, then became embedded in the culture. Storytellers emerged among the inhabitants and it was Daniel who first remarked that they ought to appoint someone to act as an historian. A scribe for the community. They might not be able to leave anything else behind. The resolution passed.

## THE BOOK OF HISTORIES AND HIVES

*Please share some part of your story here. I want us to start collecting histories.* –Jane

*Daniel Emory Woolcott, Colonel. U.S. Army, 54673*

I was born in Bloomington, Illinois. My parents were James and Emily Woolcott. I joined the Army when I turned eighteen. I served in actions in the Middle East for most of my career, and I should have retired ten years ago. I hung on because I'm still in good shape and they always seemed to have a job for me.

I was assigned to Fort Leonard Wood during the outbreak. Initially, I was assigned command of a regiment stationed here for the evacuation of the city centers of Missouri and part of Kansas. That plan went immediately to hell and we had refugees flown in from all over, mostly doctors and scientists. This place became a lab center where they tried to figure this thing out. They failed in their efforts. There was a rash of desertions and another of suicides. I served with some fine men and women, but I am the only one left of the people who were brought here by medevac. I dug a lot of holes.

I lost contact with my wife and grown children almost as soon as I got here. Communications broke down all over the country and the cell network was the worst of it. The last time I spoke to Maude, I didn't think I had any reason to say goodbye. She was in Savannah, and I don't think I have any reason to go looking. I don't have many reasons at all.

I helped to form the first council here because there was work that needed doing and people need structure. My training helps me keep focused while everyone is losing their heads. It was the right thing to do. We have order, and outside they have nothing.

My last orders from the United States government instructed me to pray. I have always followed orders.

*Andrea Ramirez*

I didn't know where to start, so I looked at where other people have begun. I don't know if it matters now, but I was born in Little Rock, Arkansas. I lived there my whole life, and enrolled at UALR. I was a sophomore when everything fell apart. The CDC set up these huge tents out on the quad and the rumor was that it was a really bad strain of the flu. They were giving out flu shots and trying to get everyone to get tested, but there wasn't much information and there were protests and a lot of people refused. We got confined to our dorms when the National Guard showed up. The power and the water went out but my iPhone kept working. I got my parents to come and get me, and the Guard couldn't say no to that. They took me home.

My mom got it first, then my little sister Violet, then me. Violet died first and my dad went crazy. We called and called for someone to help, and then for someone to come get the body. Cell service died and we had to bury her ourselves. I thought that was the worst thing I would have to do, but I had to bury my mom a week later. I'm always adjusting to the new worst thing.

My dad went out to find water one day, early in the morning before sunrise. I waited but he never came back. I had to go out on my own.

I made it almost a month, but I couldn't get out of the city. I was so scared. I carried a baseball bat and I only moved when I knew I wouldn't see anyone. When I ran into Mark, I assumed the worst. I hit him twice with the bat in his belly. He caught the bat and I was terrified, but he just sat down on the ground and asked me to talk to him. He convinced me and we traveled together most of that year. He got us out of Arkansas and we headed toward Tennessee. Everywhere we went, all we saw was men. A lot of them were dangerous and most of them wanted me. Mark killed for me. I thought that was going to be hard to live with, but it's not.

Mark got swept away by the spring floods and I couldn't save him. I barely got away myself. I was so depressed after that, I don't know how I lived through it. I met Kacie that summer, and she tried to teach me how to keep a few guys on a string, to protect me and take care of me. Kacie had five guys. One of them was pretty old, maybe in his forties. The rest were ok. People here at the Fort call it a Hive. Kacie said it was just the natural reaction to things. She was a grad student in anthropology, so I guess she'd know. I could never get used to it. She asked me to join them, and said we could pick up some more guys for me, no problem. I didn't like it. I should have stayed. I didn't know how bad things could get.

When I left them I headed north and I think I was in Kentucky but maybe it was Illinois. I was alone for a long time. I've heard some of the other women here tell how they dressed like men and I wish I'd thought of that. I didn't even cut my hair.

When the slave traders found me I figured I would die. They beat the shit out of me and raped me for days. They had one other girl, Chandra. They traded us both for a gas station, but then they came back in the middle of the night to steal us from the two guys who bought us. They killed them and we lived at the gas station for a long time. They brought in cars and motorcycles from all over and used them to bring stuff back. We had a motel to sleep in and thank god I was there the night they blew up the station. I don't know how they did it and I don't care. It gave me enough of a diversion to run away. I don't know if Chandra made it.

I didn't know I was pregnant until I got here. Dr. Jane says not to get my hopes up. I know. I told her I'll take anything after the baby dies. If I make it. I don't ever want to do this again. I don't care if none of the babies live. We don't deserve it, as a species. Evolution.

*Barry Rangel*

I am so glad I found this place. I thought I would never see anything like civilization again. A community, a society, a group of people getting along together just means so much.

Chicago fell apart faster than I would have ever imagined. If I hadn't been with the highway patrol, if I hadn't had guns, I don't know what would have happened to me. I had nobody to worry about but myself, so I headed into the city. What a nightmare! I'll never forget it. Buildings on fire and screaming and dead bodies in the street. I saw someone lynched from a telephone pole, I couldn't make any sense of that. People saw my uniform and started asking for my help, but I didn't know what I could do. Then people started to try to steal my gun and I just took off. I don't know what I owed those people, but I had to run.

I stopped to get some food in a store in Springfield one day and that's where I saw my first Hive. This woman was very smart. She looked at me like she was a spider and I was a fly, but she was calling herself Queen B. They had a beautiful house, a mansion really. There was a gas generator and they were bringing in fuel from all over. They had tons of food and guns and a really great setup. There must have been forty guys in and out of there, I don't know why she wanted to add more men to the mix.

I guess there's no reason to lie. I wasn't married, no girlfriend. I had nobody to turn my back on. I stayed there for a while. I wouldn't say I got to know her well. I know her real name was Bonnie and she was an actress. She was good-looking. Red headed and green-eyed, and she was really good in bed, the kind of thing a man dreams about. I told her I had never slept with a white woman before. She laughed and told me there were no firsts left. I still had a couple.

I never had group sex before, or any kind of sex with a man. We would work all day and pretty much fuck all night. It wasn't the worst setup I've ever seen. I would do it again, if someone started a Hive here. Especially if it was Tamara. But I really wanted something more. I knew we wouldn't be able to get gas forever, or find food forever. Bonnie wasn't interested in farming, and she said she had her tubes tied. There wasn't a future there.

That all seems like a dream I had now. Hive life is like something out of Penthouse letters, but like from the Mad Max world. I'm here and I can still have a good time with a couple of the people I know, but I also have a job. I have a community and a life here. That's what I came for.

*Mariah Sweeney*

I never thought I would be the kind of woman who has a Hive.

I was too old, to begin with. Forty when the shit hit the fan, and not very good looking. It just kind of happened.

I was living outside of Oshkosh. I never got sick. My Davy brought home our neighbor, Gus Szalinsky and my brother in law Jerry. We were all scared together and had to stay pretty close. Both of their wives had died, and we had lost our Nina. No kids, all of us worried about the same thing, it was bound to happen. Davy was jealous at first, and he couldn't be around me and Jerry. But eventually it was all four of us together. It felt like we were a family. And I could end any fight and solve any problem and make everybody feel better by just laying us all down.

When Phil joined us, I was starting to feel like it was too many men. Then we added Hank, Jax, and Matt. Jax was only sixteen years old. He was so beautiful and so young, and I never thought he'd want to sleep with me. Everything got so tangled up and strange. In some ways, it's been the freest time in my life. It feels terrible to say that with my Nina dead of the fever. I miss her every day. I miss everything. It's awful and selfish and heartless, but I have to live. I'm living.

We moved on together. We ran into trouble looking for guns, that's when Gus and Matt got shot. We got a shotgun out of it but it wasn't worth it. We lost Phil right after that from some sickness. I think it was from eating bad food. It's a terrible thing to say, but he basically shit himself to death. The rest of us found our way here. They separated us to ask us some questions. I haven't seen anyone out raping or taking slaves but I guess they've seen a lot of that here. We saw murderers, so I guess it's not far off. I told them that my guys weren't like that, and that we were used to taking care of each other.

We all got a barracks together, but Davy left us last year. He wanted to be monogamous with someone, but I can't go back to that. I'm living with Jax, Hank, and Jerry.

I don't like the term Hive. I don't think of it like that. We're more like a web.

I don't know what the future will bring. I wish I could have another child. I'm not on anything, and I still get my period, but it just hasn't happened. I know none of the babies survive, but we can't stop trying. I wish Jax could get me pregnant. That's what I'd choose.

*Liana Endescu*

What we NEED around here is FAITH and HOPE and LOVE. There is no CHAPLAIN on this base. I asked Daniel from the council, he says he doesn't know what happened. It's not proper for me as a woman to represent our LORD JESUS CHRIST but I read from the BIBLE in head covering for anyone who will listen.

This was all FORETOLD in the book of REVELATION. The SEAL was opened and a PLAGUE was loosed upon the Earth. That means the ANTICHRIST walks among us. Even now his MARK is being put upon those who would trade in the MARKETPLACE.

But we are like the FAITHLESS, those who could not watch an HOUR with the SAVIOR, or like Thomas who had to put his

HAND upon the LORD to make sure he was REAL, or like the men in the boat when CHRIST calmed the waters. Where is our FAITH?

AMERICA will be SAVED. Our CHILDREN will be DELIVERED ONLY unto us when we are WORTHY. Amen.

*Kylie Westwood*

My mommy's name was West wood. Mommy is gone now. But I want to keep it. I live with Callie. I came here with Callie when I was a baby. I don't remember. She tells me stories. I like her stories. I don't like the farm because it is dirty. I like candies that the raiders bring in. I read story books and I like airplanes. I want to see a airplane. I want to fly in a airplane. I like stories about the city from before. They are funny. I love my Callie. I want a kitty. And a puppy. And a panda. Like in the stories. That is all for now. P.S. I hate Ryan. Ryan is stupid.

*Archie Sinclair*

I know what she wants me to talk about. I get asked about it all the time. I'm not gay. I never was gay. I like women. I was married to a woman for fourteen years. I was born straight, and I chose to act gay like anybody else can choose. That's all there is to it.

I've been with Brian for more than a year now. We were friends at first, and I started to notice how kinda feminine he is. He was gay and I knew that, but we were still good friends. He could cook real good and he wasn't all faggoty in front of me.

I woke up in the middle of the night one time and heard him jacking off. That was gross and I yelled at him about it. But it happened again a couple of times and soon we were doing it at the same time. And then together.

This never would have happened if there were still women around. This is like what happens in prison, kinda. I told Brian to grow his hair out long and he did. He dresses like a woman for me when I ask him to. He tells me he loves me and he cooks for me and keeps my house and acts like a woman in bed. I don't love him that way, but he's a comfort to me. He told me a few months ago I could call him Breezy. I do, sometimes.

I can't live like those guys who are in the Hives. It's gross, it's like eating food that someone else has chewed up first. That just isn't right, no matter how hot a woman is or how rare they are. It's not natural.

What I have with Brian isn't natural either, but at least I know he's all mine.

Doc Jane says I don't have to call myself gay. I don't know what we should call it but I want us to get married. I told the raiders to keep an eye out for a nice diamond ring. I want to make an honest wife out of my Breezy.

## THE BOOK OF THE DREAMLESS ONES

Not nameless. Whole bunch of them have names, but not always. But they are dreamless. Don't suffer, don't toil. Hearts never broken. Whole and perfect. Keeping track.

Nobody, child of Shawna

Nobody and No one, children of Jenna

Nobody Obermeyer, son of Jodi and Honus Obermeyer

Gwen, daughter of Andrea. Gang-raped by slavers. Put them down. Andrea a week after the birth.

Nobody, son of Magdalena

Rhiannon, daughter of Miranda, lived two whole hours of agony

Nobody, daughter of Hannah

Carlos, son of Carlos, carried in dead after the mother died outside of St. Louis

Nobody, daughter of that girl who never spoke. Showed up pregnant. Cut.

Stephen, son of Devon. Stillborn.

Hope, daughter of Liana. Fucking terrible name for a stillborn.

Ayaan, son of Rajnigandha. Raj two days later.

John, son of Marie

Maternal death is better this year, getting better all the time. Not a selling point.

Nobody, son of Mackenzie. Mackenzie within hours. Cut.

Martha, daughter of Hannah. Hannah made it. Again.

Jeremy, son of Abigail. Abby bled out, no fever.

Nobody, child of Miranda. Early miscarriage.

Hope, daughter of Liana. Again. Fucking stop with that name.

Tyson, son of Miri. Lived long enough to get everyone's hopes up. Shit.

Nobody, child of Miri. Early miscarriage.

Nobody, child of Miri. Another one. She won't take anything.

Jill, daughter of Marie. Marie immediately. Female population down. No one coming in this winter.

Women that come from south of here are mostly cut. Handful of groups doing it, and individuals who have caught on. Slavers. Furthest anyone came was Alex from Canada. Knew he was dying of radiation sickness. One of the reactors up there gone bad, he said. Mostly from Texas, some from the east, the rest from the south. Nobody from the west at all.

# Chapter Thirteen

When Jane had been at Fort Nowhere for fifteen years, the population of the world had leveled off. People all over died of infected wounds and disease. Women and children died in childbirth, but the fury to impregnate had dimmed somewhat. Death slowed down. People had migrated and coalesced into settlements and villages, pooling knowledge and resources. They lit candles against the dark and waited. Without birth, life is only that wait.

* * * * *

The Seoul settlement was by far the most successful. Their quarantine had begun very early. Over time, they walled off the heart of the city and stopped accepting refugees. Murder and disease had persuaded them that it wasn't worth it. A rotating schedule of sex was created for the inhabitants, and every month they waited to see who would get pregnant. They had a hundred births in that time, but no success.

* * * * *

Another successful group endured in the interior of Papua New Guinea, where life had reverted to a very simple tribal organization with stunning speed. The villages came together and absorbed foreign tourists and merchants. They hunted and gathered and farmed pigs. They believed their children would be returned to them. Hundreds lived in relative safety and comfort. It was the same wait.

* * * * *

In countries that had practiced female infanticide, the tipping point had been reached much faster. In China, Pakistan, and India the number of women remaining was miniscule. Most of them lived out their lives without ever seeing the sun, or a person besides the man or men who held them. Those that got free did not get far. The most populous country on earth became a land of ghosts.

* * * * *

Island nations fared well. England and Ireland were covered with Hives. Slavers were killed in public when they were caught, and their heads were displayed on castle walls. A small army of women ranged across Wales taking heads on horseback, led by a woman who called herself Buddug.

* * * * *

The cities stopped burning. The stars filled the skies of places that hadn't seen them since man started burning coal. Herd animals took the plains. Salmon swelled the rivers. The earth grew quiet and everything seemed to teem with life and hold its breath, waiting.

* * * * *

Daniel Woolcott died that year. He died slowly, in bed. It was not where he wanted to be.

Jane sat with him, her book in her lap. She was patiently writing the names of everyone he could remember who had died at Fort Nowhere, from the beginning. The ones who had died in her infirmary she knew. Their names were in the book. Woolcott's memory was good. When he said Jack's name, Jane's heart stopped. She asked him where he had buried the dead.

When he was gone, she went out to Potter's Field and buried her cell phone. She had carried it from San Francisco. From that time, she had only her phone, her knife, and her book. The phone would never be useful again, and she left it for Jack. It used to connect them. It was only a symbol, but she thought that it might connect them again. She couldn't cry. She left the field without anything to say that would sum it all up.

Jax was elected to council to take Daniel's place. Jax had taken Mariah's last name, and so he was Jax Sweeney. Mariah was still alive, and Jax was one of three.

The next year, Jane saw Colleen through another pregnancy. Colleen was living with Bart and Eric, she said it could be either one of theirs. Jane furrowed her greying eyebrows and looked at her mutilated genitals, ready to confirm what the woman already knew.

"You're pregnant. About two months, I'd say."

"Yeah."

"Can you still have an orgasm?"

"I'm not sure. I think I never had one before. I still enjoy sex, though."

Take that away with a knife. I dare you.

Jane nodded. "I'll want to see you every month, if you're going to keep it. If you're not, you should decide soon."

Colleen shrugged. "What's the point of aborting now?"

"Not getting sick. Not getting torn open. Not dying of the fever that pops up after."

"Nobody has died of the fever in two years." Colleen bit her lip.

"No, they haven't. It's up to you."

"I'll keep it. It'll give everyone something to talk about." Colleen fixed her skirt and stood up.

"Ok?"

"Sure." Jane walked outside with her and watched the clouds roll past, fast and low.

Jane watched Colleen's pregnancy through the summer. A group of slavers was hanged on a very hot day and the Fort gained another woman. A beautiful bald black girl named Shayla. She thought she was about twenty years old, but she wasn't sure. Her age was debated as Jane tried to place the time of her birth relative to the plague. Shayla did not remember her parents, only which she had been with a succession of men as far back as she could remember. She was very smart and could read. She wanted to be trained as a nurse. Jane took her on and taught her the basics of midwifery using Colleen as an example.

Colleen went into labor during the coldest part of the year. The two men she lived with had to dig snow out of the door of the infirmary to bring her in. Jane came in and sent them to get Shayla. Neither one of them wanted to stay. Jane understood.

They scrubbed their hands.

"Have you seen a baby born?"

"No."

"You been doing the reading?"

"Yes. But the reading doesn't explain about the fever."

"The fever is new and the books are old. I want you to assist me, and if you have any questions you can ask. Try to keep Colleen calm. You know she's cut, right?"

"I know. Glad I'm not."

"You and me both."

Colleen was on a low bed, laying on her side. She moaned a little and Jane could see her belly cramping.

"Is that how you're most comfortable?"

Colleen nodded.

Shayla brought cold snowy water without being asked and sat quietly. Colleen drank.

Jane watched and waited. When Colleen shifted her weight, she checked for dilation.

"We're halfway there. Drink some more, ok?"

Colleen took tiny sips. "I want to give the baby a name."

"That's fine, most people do."

"I've been trying not to think about it." Her face crimped into a series of lines as another contraction hit. She breathed through it. "But today's the day, so I think I will."

"Sure. Shayla, will you get me the laudanum?" Jane had distilled the drug herself out of poppies that had been brought back from a raid and cultivated on the grounds. Laudanum tincture was not morphine, but it was better than nothing. She worried more about antibiotics, which she had not yet managed to synthesize.

Shayla came back with the cobalt blue glass bottle. Jane set it down and waited.

Colleen tossed and turned. She could not get comfortable. Jane watched.

"When she's ready, she'll get into a position that lets gravity help us. Just let her be." Jane spoke in a low voice to Shayla. Shayla was still.

When Colleen shifted up to her hands and knees, Jane rolled her chair in close and motioned for Shayla to do the same.

"Alright, Colleen, it's crowning. I can see it. A couple more hard pushes and you've got it."

Colleen bore down, making a low powerful sound. Her hand flew without her volition to touch the baby's head. She pushed again and the baby gushed free, slipping into Jane's hands.

The child cried right away, loud and lusty. Jane sighed. It was so much worse when they cried, when the little cries faded away to silence. She laid the baby down naked at the foot of the bed and addressed herself to Colleen and to Shayla.

"Now we deliver the placenta and try to stop the bleeding."

"I want to hold her, giver her to me!" Colleen was sobbing and trying to turn herself over.

"Colleen, it will be harder if… shit. Fine. Ok." Jane wrapped the still-crying baby in a towel. She didn't look the child in the face. She did not ask how Colleen knew she had given birth to a girl. She laid the bundle in Colleen's lap when she was right and Colleen prepared to nurse the child.

Jane watched, detached. It wouldn't hurt either of them. She thought it was a terrible idea, but she couldn't stop it. Colleen was running on wordless instinct. Trying to get in the way of it would be as pointless as trying to halt birth once it had begun.

Colleen yelped a little as the girl latched on. She contracted again and the placenta rushed forth.

"Watch that and tell me when it stops pulsing."

Shayla looked pale, but she nodded and her eyes only strayed to the baby a few times as she watched. Jane cut the cord when the pulsing had stopped and wrapped the placenta in a towel. Gently, slowly they moved Colleen to a clean bed. The baby continued to nurse. Jane had not cleaned an infant in twenty years. She remembered how, and looking now she thought she should. She waited.

Colleen's child fell away from the nipple, obviously asleep. The three women sat in silence, watching her and waiting for her breath to stop. No one said a word for a long time.

Dawn surprised everyone but Jane. She was still awake, still staring at the little bundle as it went on breathing. Colleen had slept with her arms around the baby, as natural as anything. Jane had checked them both for fever a dozen times. Shayla had dozed in her chair.

Jane thought she counted six hours since this baby was born. This was longer than any baby had lasted so far. She put a hand on Shayla's shoulder and the girl stirred.

"Heat up some water and bring me more clean towels, please."

Jane had to coax Colleen into letting go.

"Don't take her! She's still breathing! Just let me hold her until she stops!"

"It's ok. It's ok. I'm going to clean her up and look her over, that's all." She took the child and Colleen cried softly.

Jane bathed the baby there in the room where Colleen could see. The child cried the quick, sharp cry of a newborn. She did not like the cold when the air touched her wet skin, and Jane knew she didn't like being away from her mother. The baby was clean, dusky pink, perfectly formed, and alive. She swaddled the baby tight into a towel and took her back to Colleen.

"I think she's hungry again," Colleen said, opening her blouse. Jane and Shayla stared.

They did not tell anyone that day. The infirmary doors stayed closed and no one came to call. Births were given a solemn silence so that everyone might grieve. It was usual for no one to come for three days or more.

On the third day, Colleen asked for Bart and Eric. Jane walked

Shayla to the door.

"Don't tell anyone. Hear me? Don't even tell those two. Just tell them she wants them to come. Ok?"

Shayla nodded and went out the door.

Jane left the room when the men came in. She wished for coffee. Coffee was long gone. She ached all over. It was exhaustion, it was envy, it was the atrophied muscle of optimism stirring to activity once again.

*Midwinter*

Can't explain it. Don't know what we did differently. Don't know what changed or why. That kid has been alive a week and I'm still afraid to write it down. Colleen named her Rhea. Rhea Rhea Rhea the princess of this place. Raiders brought back a truckload of diapers and blankets and clothes. More than she'll ever use, but people hope this is the beginning.

Beginning. Not the end, the beginning.

If you don't know what worked, how can you do it again?

How did we do it the first time? They didn't know either and they never wrote anything down.

There is no water and no rock. There is no center and nothing holds. Fragments within and without. In the beginning, there was Rhea. Nobody will ask why ever again. She is why.

* * * * *

Rhea was not the only child on earth, but she was the first. If it can be found once, it will be found again. The population picked up, slowly. Growth would never be what it had been once. But there were children in the world. One by one, they were lost and found.

# Epilogue

Mother Ina untied her belly and hung it on the peg on her wall. She rubbed the back of her neck and poured herself a glass of water. She had a good group of boys this year. They were sharp and obedient. Eager to please.

Ina lived in the House of Mothers, because she had survived the birth of a living child. It had happened to her only once, long ago. Her daughter Etta had left after she got her blood to hunt and kill slavers. She came back once a year.

The House of Mothers held thirty five women. The unnamed midwife had trained Shayla and Pauline, they had trained Emily and Tobyn. Emily had died in childbirth, Tobyn had taught Judith, Gabrielle, and Linda who had made the Law of Emily: Mothers could not be Midwives. The separation of women had begun in their time.

Ina's child had been delivered by Bailey, acolyte of Judith. Etta was blessed at birth so that her spirit would be strong. Ina hoped that she would tie the hollow belly around her daughter's waist when her time came. Etta had chosen another life.

Etta brought back lost children every year. She brought back girls, cut and uncut. She brought back women, Mothers and Midwives. Etta was a great hunter, but she did not bring back men. People talked about that, but nothing was done.

Every year Etta came to the gates of Nowhere and gave the signal that allowed her to pass. She went first to the shrine of the Unnamed Midwife. There she laid offerings from the old world on the altars of Colleen, Rhea, and She the Unnamed. Only then would she seek out Ina. They were as uneasy with one another as two strangers. Etta treated every man in her mother's household as though he were her father. It was the respectful thing to do.

She was out there now, Ina knew. She kept her own book and carried her own guns. Ina stared at the belly on the wall and counted the days. She sat down to her own copy of The Book of the Unnamed Midwife to read a little before going to sleep.

*Spring*

All Jack's notes are tucked into the back cover of this book. Read them so many times I could recite them. Coincidence. Like lightning hitting the same place twice. Happens. Bury me there. Together.

Didn't have it figured out, even with the lab equipment that I can't run without power. Had some proteins, some ideas for a cure. All recorded failures. Colleague's notes all the same. None of them had it figured.

Maybe Shayla was born after the epidemic. Maybe she's the baby Carter was carrying. Maybe the Andrea who died here on my table is the same Andrea who left that note. Maybe Duke and Roxanne will ride their Harleys here one day and Jodi will lead her dozens of children to my door. Maybe there was a plan maybe it's all connected maybe Rhea will walk on water and raise the dead.

Only won by forfeit or default. Not because we really understand, or because we deserve it. Couldn't slay the dragon. Don't know why it worked or how we did it. Can't explain method=can't replicate results. No science. Just my jaw down and my eyes open, just the sound of that baby crying and the whole village coming to see.

Three more are ready to pop before summer is out. Passing Rhea around like a good luck charm. Rub the good baby on you, make it stick.

In the absence of science we have folk magic. We don't know why it works but it worked before. Working again. Midwives, working again.

Victory?

Victory.

# Author Bio

Meg Elison is a graduate of UC Berkeley and lives with her husband and tribe in Oakland, California. She can be found one the periodic table somewhere between iron and silver.

The author was a columnist for The Daily Californian, and has been published in Caliber Magazine, and Promise of Berkeley. Her poetry has been published in "Flight" 2009 and 2010, "Scribendi" 2012, "From the Four-Chambered Heart: In Tribute to Anaïs Nin," and "Alternate Lanes: An Anthology of Travel Using Alternate Transportation in the City of Angels." Her blog is available at paganmeghan.com. She is currently at work on a sequel to *The Book of the Unnamed Midwife.* @paganmeghan

## Titles by Sybaritic Press

L.A. Melange: the first year of poeticdiversity
*from the editors of poeticdiversity*
ISBN #0971223289
$10.00
Nihilistic Foibles by *Marie Lecrivain*
ISBN #9780977867066
$10.00
Stories From the Inside Edge by *Brenda Petrakos*
ISBN #09780977867073
$12.00
Naked In Paradise by *Len Richmond*
ISBN #9781604615999
$11.99
A Soldier's Fate by *D.L. Warner*
ISBN #9781606438466
$11.99
Antebellum Messiah by *Marie Lecrivain*
ISBN #9781615319659
$11.00
Ensnared Volume I by *D.L. Warner*
ISBN #9781450798303
$12.99
Bitchess by *Marie Lecrivain*
ISBN #9781450789455
$10.00
Alternate Lanes by *Marie Lecrivain and the staff of poeticdiversity*
ISBN #9781467546546
$9.95
Love Poems Yes...Really...Love Poems by *Marie Lecrivain*
ISBN #9781467562423
$11.99
From the Four-Chambered Heart edited by *Marie Lecrivain*
ISBN #978-1467581363
$12.95
Diary of the Last Person on Earth by *Robert King*
ISBN #978-1495100420
$12.99
Near Kin edited by *Marie Lecrivain*
ISBN #978-1495105524
$12.99

50745508R00115

Made in the USA
Charleston, SC
06 January 2016